DADDY
BOY

Published in 2023 by Cipher Press
105 Ink Court
419 Wick Lane
London, E3 2PX

Paperback ISBN: 978-1-7392207-4-7
eBook ISBN: 978-1-7392207-5-4

Published in agreement with McSweeny's, San Francisco

Printed and bound in the UK by TJ Books

Distributed by Turnaround Publisher Services

Cover Design by Carly Murphy-Merrydew
Typeset by Laura Jones

www.cipherpress.com

DADDY BOY

EMERSON WHITNEY

Cipher press

To Hank

Clouds on all sides were sucking in on themselves. Hank was driving the car through locusts.

Paintball pelts of yellow streaked everywhere, closing up the windshield. The sound of it was soft like someone sticking Solo cups in chainlink. He was laughing and driving eighty or ninety. Tye, in the front seat, bit his middle finger and played like he was bored. Nobody could see and nobody cared. Hank kept his body relaxed. He drove like he was driving a bus and was about to wave to people. The light glowed through the bugs that were making mud of themselves across the car. The only smell was a grassy one from the insects dying and the five-in-one shampoo that the boys all shared.

DADDY BOY

There were four of us in the car. I had a Tech Deck in my pocket that I never played with, I just kept it around like a key. I was listening to Nelly on my Discman and Hank was driving through the locusts, laughing, saying, you know they're trying to eat each other, right?

I've been thinking about locusts when they swarm. It's true what Hank said, that they swarm because of turning cannibal. They're hungry for each other and they're being eaten at the same time. They're chasing and running. Each one realizes it like threading tape, like legs getting plied apart. I haven't seen a locust in so long. I dream about them often, little desperate streaks on the windshield. I wet my fingers with my tongue.

Hank had won a trip to Orlando by putting a piece of paper into a box by the register at a Tom Thumb in Dallas, that's where we were going. I'd won something the same way about a year prior from the same Tom Thumb, it was a holiday stocking that was red and mesh and full of old candy. When my mom wasn't looking, I'd registered to win and they called and I remember her waving her arm to ask me over to the phone. What did you do? she'd waved. But I'd won. I picture Hank putting the piece of paper in the cardboard box for fun, his only pastime is drafting. The pads of his hands always have pencil smudges on them.

Hank has such a specific smell. This is probably his hair. He has a lot of shaggy hair. He uses ripped towels after the shower and keeps unhooked appliances all throughout his house from different projects getting worked on everywhere. In the winter, he puts a tree together in the living room and hangs a plastic cranberry wreath on the door. He has a drafting table that takes up nearly the whole floorspace of his bedroom. There're blueprint papers everywhere. The dog's tail hits the tubes the papers go in.

Whenever I visit, I follow him to his jobs. He works endlessly and I go with him to whatever site he's working on and everyone says we look so much alike. This is only a coincidence.

Tom Thumb paid for our flight and our hotel, it wasn't for Disney, just for Orlando itself. Hank wanted to take us, we hadn't ever been on a trip just the four of us, my two brothers and Hank. It was spring. We rented a red Chevy Blazer at the Orlando airport and drove toward a circular hotel with rooms that opened onto a font of fake indoor plants.

My brothers, Gunner and Tye, look like Hank, the three of them have that hair. They're bonded. Tye is stylish these days with nice sunglasses. Gunner and I have the same eyebrows and nose, we're shaped a little more similarly, but he's still all Hank undeniably. I'm much smaller and my knuckles are a darker color and my face has different kinds of bones. Tye and Gunner play a lot of games together (it used to be Magic Cards, and then some kind of intense video game). I never know what they're talking about. They're best friends. I bumped around with Gunner in the backseat. We had a ways to go, along two-lane highways with swamp nearby. It was just a straight road and then the cloud of locusts.

In general, Hank was always laughing, saying things like, it's all fun and games until someone loses an eye and then it's just a game to try and find the eye.

This is the guy who gets so angry when I say I don't know where I'm from. Texas, goddamn it! You motherfucker, you're from Texas! and he laughs the whole time, saying somehow I'm the only one of his children born in the state, except he wasn't even there when I was born.

I'm thinking about "Pop."

Like the meaning of it that's "to appear."

I've got pictures like this: I'm staring at my mom, and Dad's face just comes over, hovers near her shoulder, and it's a surprise— they broke up when I was eighteen months old. I used to call him my "bio-dad" but I don't even know what that means.

"O father" says Etymology Online about the origins of "papa."

Whenever we talk about it, my grandma tells me this story about my dad and how she'd buy him chocolate milk and he'd use small medicinal amounts of it in regular milk to make it last until it went bad. She also tells me that my first word was either dad or dog and that he'd dress me up in little pink outfits with black buckle shoes and carry me everywhere. We moved in with my mom's parents on the East Coast when I was two weeks old because my dad had lost his job in Dallas. He started working the front desk at a gym and would take me to his shift sometimes. He was always bouncing you, she says.

Honestly, I've spent most of my life thinking I was missing this: I only know my dad through photos on social media. I have screenshots of the photos saved on my phone. He has puppies on his chest in one and I've looked at it and wondered what it would feel like to be near him. He wears a little straw cowboy hat in these photos. We both have short torsos and are sweet-looking I think. He's little. I want to know what kind of soap his is. I see people sometimes that look like him and want to go up and talk. I remember when I had athlete's foot a lot as a kid, he'd told me that he'd had that too. We 've both had ankle injuries on the right side. Both of us will pick up trash if it's around.

How is it that I feel like it was me who left him?

How is it that I feel like the one who ended things? He and my mom broke up when I was eighteen months old. Thinking back on it, I imagine experiencing a supreme loss of strength. I imagine it gone.

This is important:

On our way to school or on errands, Hank liked to scream for no reason.

DADDY BOY

He drove a big black Navigator pickup or sometimes a silver one because the cars came from his job.

We 'd go behind the strip mall where the boys got haircuts, the one with Target and the Cici's Pizza. It was a busy mall but desolate in the back. Hank would be between gigs when we 'd do this, or on the way to Home Depot. I'd practice driving for a half hour or two.

Once, while pretending to parallel park back there, I cut somebody off by accident and a guy with blond tips in an open Jeep Wrangler pulled up right to the passenger window to get angry. Hank yelled something about trying to teach his kid to drive and what the fuck man and the guy was like, let's get out and I'll show you whatever and motioned to take off his seat belt. Hank was like let me show you something and he turned to this mouth-faced guy, blew him a kiss, and then put his hand on the wheel and his foot on my foot and pressed it down. It was my first time driving us home from the parking lot and it was okay.

When he'd pick me up from school it was always several hours late and I didn't care. One out of every five times I'd get in the car, I'd put my backpack down between my knees and we'd drive a few blocks and then he'd bloodcurdle scream. There'd be cars all around but no kids anymore. What were we training for? He'd shriek randomly. The scream would start in my head and go through my hands.

This book is the back of a wide open mouth.

Am I yelling?

I like this image of an open mouth like made with reckless brushstrokes in a painting, a mouth that's also a cloud. Its base widening, purple and pregnant.

I want to live inside of changing conditions. No departure, no arrival, just a wide, whipped-up pause.

Here's the question: how to live without resolution. This question is a photo of myself standing beneath this shaking cloud. I realize I'm all tangled. I want to relate to this tangle without untangling, without setting fire.

I realize in writing this book, I might also be trying to feel better about myself. I have a small frame, legs that spread out slightly when I sit. I take pictures of myself shirtless from my computer after I shower. I don't post any of them. I look at the red splotches on my body and massage them. This is the moon to me, this surface. It's devastating, the link between the hunk that I move around in and my consciousness. What bridge is this? I used to slice at it, I was one of those kids who'd bend a paper clip apart. I'd do it slowly so it wasn't obvious. I would make a sharp point, sharp enough to scab my tongue if I sucked on it, its pink plastic loosened into sheaths like bark. I'd nod at you while you were talking and stick the pin-end of it into my hand until it left a swelled hole that turned bright orange.

DADDY BOY

You don't know me like this.

I haven't behaved like this for years.

You know me as someone who walks upright and loves people and moves softly through the snow. All of this is true. Still, there's a residue.

The plains make a mess of me and still, I come. I have come.

I wonder what I want in a very loud way, out loud, like why did I come back here? I asked it but I said it.

Do you know what I mean by the plains? I drove across the US a few times and, each time, found myself wanting to take pictures of the backs of the gas stations. Hank and Tye and Gunner and I lived across the street from a 7-Eleven. The lights still do something to me. The grass is always waving in the back, bugs make their way up the air machines with their hum, the colors are always simple at the gas station and primary. The flowers are patient and brushed. The black rubber mats come out at night and get washed. A slushee machine rotates. The plains are flat as fuck. It's dry, sometimes there's a shallow, but rarely. When I had to go to Y day camp while Mom worked, they'd take us to "water world," which was a field that had cracking grasshoppers and a shade shelter and one small shallow with no water.

When I got older, I'd plow through the plains, sit pants-less in black Fords pulled onto the side of the road, Dopplers going, ugly laptops on the dashboard. I was thirteen and living in tornado chat rooms. I'd wanted to learn more about weather.

A friend of mine called one of my books a period piece because of my writing about the '90s. I guess this is part of that: I was the only one in the house who used the internet for a long time.

I'd meet random guys on there. One of the guys was the first to suggest that I should stick my finger inside myself. I hadn't thought of it.

Jared Yates Sexton, author of *The Man They Wanted Me To Be: Toxic Masculinity and a Crisis of Our Own Making*, writes about the Dallas Cowboys and NASCAR and it's all so familiar, particularly when he explains that the men in his family who loved the Cowboys and NASCAR also loved Evel Knievel and how all three trade in this sense of rockstar masculinity that comes from acting contrary "to principals of self-preservation."

The boys loved Evel Knievel growing up, it was basically Jackass but just one guy and they'd all crowd around the TV while Hank played videos of the guy in his red, white, and blue outfits with that big '70s collar revving a motorcycle on a ramp that would launch him over a long row of cars. I didn't want to watch. It wasn't fun to feel that adrenaline.

I didn't like being around things like that. I hate scary movies of all kinds. I wouldn't watch Braveheart with them or Gladiator. I could never figure out if I wanted Tye, Gunner, and Hank to be different or if I wanted to be.

Hannah Arendt in *On Violence* says something about how proximity to death increases our vitality.

I always have to remind myself that the most dangerous thing I ever did storm chasing was meeting those guys from the chat rooms when I was a teenager.

The internet spreads out like prairie.

I hadn't lied to myself about it this time.

I have always wanted to do this thing where I describe the plains. I want to just describe them, some of these images, these locust ones. I don't belong, really, is the feeling.

You know when Joan Didion went to the dam or whatever? I'm doing that I decided.

I decided it from inside a tent in my backyard in Los Angeles, where I was living at the time. This was 2017. It had taken weeks to arrive. It was canvas and ten by twelve and I set it up on top of the concrete extension of driveway that abutted our neighbor's yellow, neglected 4Runner. My ex and I had lived together for almost nine years in a series of places. We'd been together a third of my life. This duplex was the last place we'd share and I was now sleeping in the backyard because we'd started hating each other. The tent was the glamping kind. Actually, it was the military kind that has recently become the glamping kind. I'd set it up after going to the Ikea in Burbank for a futon and a desk. When Jo and I moved to LA, rent for a one bedroom was actually okay, but not anymore. It was cheaper to furnish a tent than to move out. I also wasn't sure I was moving out. I drove back from Ikea with a super small futon that somehow fit in my Corolla with the doors slightly open.

It was May and I kept thinking about how it was definitely storming somewhere. I'd check the radar to see how much it was storming in Texas. There was no safety from the sun in LA. The light was violent. No clouds had come by in forever. I was so tired of squinting. I'd check the weather in Texas again and again, it had become compulsive.

The whole reason I was in the tent was because I'd begun to want things I'd never let myself want before.

It was odd, it sort of seeped in.

Out of nowhere, I'd begun wanting to pull a person toward my pelvis, to watch my arms flex while I did it. I wanted to feel someone else in my hands. This switch wasn't allowed in my relationship. This is why we'd started hating each other. Originally, all I wanted to do was follow a more powerful person around and do the dishes for her or carry her bag. It was nice to be looked at, to be held by the chin and wanted.

Jo and I went to a couple's therapy session about this just before I moved into the tent. It was one of the last things we did together. I picked the counselor because she was vaguely a friend of both of ours and that felt nice. She asked Jo if she could ever let me top.

I winced when the counselor asked it because I needed her to do the asking and I hadn't realized it until then, which very much felt like bottom behavior. I was a mattress with change dropped onto it.

The feeling had started small, like the smallest pearl of an irritant, when I would do something that had originally turned me on, like ask what can I do to make your day better Daddy and doing what she wanted when she wanted it, or even better, anticipating that.

My ex, a full-time domme, had always argued that the bottom really was the powerful one, was the fulcrum for the whole thing. That was me, I guess.

But, in the counseling office, she'd just laughed. The therapist looked at me for a split second sort of stunned, then shrugged and said, I think you got your answer Emerson.

Jo and I had been in a lifestyle S-M relationship the whole time we'd been together. Our "play" had slowed by that point to less public pain stuff, but still once a month we had a date where she used the single tail on me or something. I'd been obsessed with the pain part at the beginning. She'd pierce my whole back, then thread a string through the piercings and tie it to the ceiling during a play party. I'd wear nothing but boxers and long socks and would be smiling the whole time, totally sober, just all lit up by pain.

At her fortieth birthday, another domme pierced my arms up and down and put candles on my piercings for Jo to blow out. We were at a small club in New York City and her friend did a slow and careful job in the hallway and I walked back into the crowd glowing from the candles with no blood at all anywhere because these dommes are incredible at what they do. Jo's face twisted as I got close and I thought maybe it was me. I looked down at the cake I was holding, and then at her face. She brightened for me, but later she got mad at her friend because piercing me was her job. I wasn't in trouble though because in this framework, where I had no agency, I couldn't be in trouble. I'd loved this. It was so relieving to not really be able to do wrong.

You know how amazing that feels? But after years of this, almost ten years, it had started to hurt. It's weird, but especially after we got married, it started to hurt. Like physically. I have Ehlers–Danlos and am in pain all the time, and Jo would talk about how all masochists are alike, all her clients had pain of some kind, either childhood or adult pain issues that they had to transform into pleasure. She'd talk about the client who had his leg in a twist, which doctors attempted to readjust with a metal brace that they'd tighten once a week during his childhood in the '50s—she had a lot of clients like this, she'd say. He'd been lying there as a kid having to change his mind about what he felt—to find that soft line between pleasure and pain—because there was nowhere else to go. When masochism started to hurt it wasn't like my pain had ended, that's not going anywhere (my neck isn't hooked on right)—but something else had started to happen, I didn't really know what it was.

"Jumping the Shark"—that phrase—came from Evel Knievel and I guess also the Fonz from *Happy Days*. For Evel's part, by the time of his last ever jump thirty years before his death, he'd become super cautious and had started not wanting to die.

For his last jump, on a trial run, he supposedly crashed into a cameraperson and broke two arms and took out the cameraperson's eye—these details may have been rumors spread by Evel himself, either way, the jump itself wasn't all that interesting. A bunch of the sharks in the pool that he was jumping over had been sedated, a number of them died after the sedation.

This is an aside: I was on the varsity softball team in high school (Hank would come to my games, he's still proud that

I'm his only child who'd play sports). But I only "lettered" because I was the kid willing to get hit with pitches. When there'd be an important play and someone needed to advance, they'd send me out there to square up for a bunt and try and get hit with that giant neon softball to advance the runner. I didn't mind at all.

What is the point of all this?

When Jo would wind up with the flogger or the single tail, I'd started to see the force she had to pull into her body in order to hit my body like that. I'd started to wince. I would want it to be over. She was okay with this slowing down and ending, the sadomasochist part at least, but she'd still wanted to be in charge.

I'd liked our life. I gazed out at the lemon tree in the yard. I'd liked looking at it from our bed. I was looking past it now, watching her from my futon. She didn't look any different than she always had, white and muscled and tattooed. I was supposed to be in our bed in our bedroom.

I pushed thin city wood into the portable stove. She waved at me from the bedroom window. I didn't know she could see me through the mesh tent window, it seemed opaque in the dark. I waved back.

I'd been watching her open and close our dresser drawers— her silhouette was slight against the sheer curtain.

DADDY BOY

Maybe this is the part that matters:

On my left wrist is a tattoo of the initials M. H. M. Hank told me that he would have named me after his grandmother, those are her initials. I wanted to put the name in me. It was my first tattoo.

On that same arm, just a bit further down, is a brand. It looks like I've tested positive for TB—we hadn't thought that through. It will be there for the rest of my life: three raised dots that Jo made with a cauterizing iron on that soft part of my inner arm, just before my elbow. We'd done it on a whim. I showed everyone.

I rubbed my eyes in the tent because it was 8 p.m. or something. I looked around in my sheets for socks. There were maple trees in front of the house—thin and flakey, but they were there. The sun was gone. We'd fought in the kitchen a few nights before. We'd not been decent in our fighting—fights like the kind where it gets so sour so fast, like where is that person who was making out or touching me or being alive in my life just moments before?

Fighting is psychedelic like early morning is. The kind where I can't see my own hand in front of my face. Maybe all fights are about power, but there was such an agreed upon power imbalance in our relationship that this was a new kind of argument for us. I hate those end feelings, when it's like lightning to be near each other. Like sometimes dogs can walk alongside one another just fine but then other times they open their mouths to each other's necks and need to bring the other down to be okay. I wasn't trying to bring her down. I think I was saying give me space, which maybe is the dog thing too. I hadn't wanted space before. I hadn't wanted anything besides what she wanted.

In that evening haze I saw something that for a second I thought might be lightning but turned out to be a police helicopter passing above the backyard. I felt like crying, the feeling was in my stomach. For years, I'd followed what I thought would lead me to belonging, but I still didn't have what I wanted. Was the feeling of family back where I'd left it? For the first time since I was a kid, I thought to go home. I opened my computer and typed in Dallas. I typed in May. Ride with us, this ad said. Come to north Texas. Meet in Dallas and then we go. It was an advertisement for a small storm chasing business. I'd forgotten those tours were a thing, they seemed to belong to the early 2000s.

I clicked on an image with a faux Discovery Channel font. It sent me to a page of storm chasing tours—the ones that take people into the plains, up and down Tornado Alley during the best time of year to be there (though that phrase is now becoming outdated because climate change is altering where tornadoes are most regular). The promo pictures from the tours were of happy people, different heights and skin tones, standing by wedges, by thin funnels, off the sides of the road or in it, they were in windbreakers. The site said it's for thrill seekers and I was like yes. That's me. Right now, that's me.

I found a very specific graph of all the different tornado chasing companies. I started clicking around and wondering if I could convince one to let me come for free and write about it. I crafted an email that I sent to something like seventeen different companies, with names like Tornado Extremes and Weather Warriors and pictures of big rotating radars parked next to white vans.

I told them I was a writer and I wanted to join.

I'm awful at joining. Why did I think this would be fun?

That had been Hank's biggest complaint in recent years—just try and have some fun, okay? he'd say, wishing I'd be less "militant" (his word).

We were mad at each other at the time because he and Tye had randomly been in New York for work at the same time as me. This was a few years ago. We'd decided to take a trip to see my grandparents, my mom's parents, who they hadn't seen in a very long time. Tye wanted to go see the hospital where he was born and buy sweatshirts in a random town he found on Yelp and get this pizza he'd read about, things like that, and I was exhausted by the way the car went where he told it to and how I was unable to command the group like that even just to stop somewhere to pee or to drive the rental car even though I was the only one who knew where we were going without a

GPS. Gunner joined too, because none of them had seen our grandparents in nearly a decade.

In the driveway, my grandpa wanted to take our picture and I said something like, not a photo right now, Gramps, you take them while I'm moving and my face is all blurred, and he just said, don't worry, I always cut you out of it anyway.

He was making a joke.

Hank shook my shoulder, like, oh, laugh with us, but nothing about my body would do it.

I'm not laughing because it's not funny, I'd said.

And Hank was like, oh, come on, you're so sensitive. You gonna be mad at Grandpa now? Can't take a Grandpa joke?

And Tye looked at us with his lips drawn into a tight smile like, you always lose this game.

Grandpa looked happy because he made these men laugh, but my grandma was like, let's move on you guys and gestured toward the house and my grandpa dropped his smile and went to follow her because he'd realized that she was upset and I was like, no, I'm fucking tired of all this and everyone turned to me and it wasn't a huge gesture, but I just walked away.

It was silly because I was walking down their short driveway toward the cul-de-sac and it wasn't dramatic. I pressed across the soft asphalt for a full three minutes while they watched before I could sort of hide behind the handful of trees on the island they had there.

I could have let my anger drop, but my stomach was uncomfortable and all I'd done with that feeling in the past was scratch at my own hands so I wouldn't feel it. I always feel cut out, is the thing. Now I was stuck walking around a neighborhood full of elders wondering how to return to the house without looking ridiculous. The return became way more of a problem than the walking away.

Hank was frustrated with me in an uncharacteristic way when I came back inside. He avoided eye contact, which was new. At the airport the next day, he was like, I wish you'd been able to just enjoy family. You're angry all the time, Tye was saying and nodding, it's annoying. They all laughed sitting at the Chick-fil-A kiosk at the gate.

I still haven't recovered from feeling laughed at by them because I've felt laughed at by them my whole life. I realize I was mad at Tye for dictating the trip because I'd also gotten tired of being Jo's passenger. It's funny because Jo and Tye and Gunner and Hank all got along. Whenever I questioned my relationship to Jo, I'd feel attached to their approval of my relationship. They respected me through her, it felt like. Now I was feeling a complicated set of things. Would storm chasing let me just push open the door of my relationship to Dallas with one finger and look around? Does it make sense that I keep trying?

When I wrote the storm chasing people, everybody said no to me writing, or riding along as a writer, except two. I'd been refreshing my email for days. Derek at Storm Travelers said something like a lot of these tours are red but ours is very blue. I hadn't asked about this at all. I realized they'd read about me and said it as a way of articulating queer-and-trans-friendly. Their logo was a clip art tornado in front of a rainbow flag.

I googled Derek—he was smiling with soft eyes in every photo. When he emailed back it was to ask me why I wanted to come, I found myself explaining that I grew up loving weather like other kids loved horses or whatever.

Even yesterday I sat in a parking lot across from a Texas Roadhouse in a small East Coast town, waiting for a line of storms to come in. I'd watched it on a radar from the airport after dropping my friend off. Instead of driving home, I drove toward it. I am proud when I show up at the right time and get to watch the mixture of light and sound that comes from some thundercloud growing and then letting off rain. I sat in its way and got to be a little scared when it cracked at us all, cracked right above us at the perfect angle and poured. There were other trucks in that lot idling too. Some people were snacking.

DADDY BOY

I said something about community to Derek and surprised myself—I'd be excited to be in storm chasing community, I said, and he was like great, let's do it. I didn't want that actually at all. I said it though. He told me I had to pay for all my own food and motel rooms but the tour itself would be free to me. I could even make money if I took a video that got a lot of views. And that sounded okay because I was between semesters and not making money as an adjunct anyway. I did this little dance inside the tent and texted Jo that I was going to go. She texted something nice back with a lightning bolt. I had just wanted her to like me the whole time, from the beginning through the end.

On our first date eight years earlier, we'd gone to Governors Island to look at some art. It was sculptures of genitals and it wasn't a date, she'd said, because I was way too young. I liked the idea of a free ferry ride and I loved when people said I was too young but still went out with me.

I was still thinking that maybe we'd get back together after the tour. I left all my stuff and planned to come back and continue my stay in the tent, but I'd also begun researching divorce—we'd just gotten married the previous June after all those years together.

This is what you do when you get divorced, I've learned: you go home. But home for me has always meant driving around.

I just saw an ad this morning for St. Vincent's new album.

I guess it's called *Daddy's Home*. In the ad, she says, "to become daddy is simply to become yourself and to become comfortable in your own skin."

I'm liking this idea more and more, honestly. I'm liking the idea of comfort, particularly. I'd be so excited just to be at peace in my own body. I once had a mentor tell me about ice storms, that the only way you can get a tree back to the middle after an ice storm is to push it all the way back to the other side and let it grow to the middle.

The end of things with Jo was really me starting to wonder if I wanted to be Daddy now. I was having the realization that I could, for example, buy myself birthday cake any day I wanted. I could leave dishes anywhere. I wanted agency all of a sudden.

I felt like I was getting pulled into a turbine or something. My arms were outstretched toward her and all we'd shared, but my body was going away. I imagine she might see it differently. Either way, I couldn't be hers anymore.

Basically, what I'm trying to say is, something mammoth was happening: I was aging.

I would have gotten you out of there if I could have, I really would have, you know that, right?

DADDY BOY

The faucet was dripping while Hank scooped several handfuls of empty K-Cups out of the sink. It smelled sort of like hazelnut in the room because of it. The house was full of things that Hank had no time to throw away, chewed shoes from the dog and bags of unpacked groceries. This was all part of why we hadn't visited in years, Jo didn't want to stay in a place like that. But it was familiar to me. I hadn't actually meant to be spending the night. My Storm Travelers tour started the following morning. I'd committed to it. I'd been in Dallas for just a couple of hours. I was supposed to go straight to Oklahoma City from the airport, but my flight had gotten delayed until so late, like 1 a.m. I'd called Hank when we were first flagged as delayed and said, essentially, don't worry, I'll just change my plans and stay in Dallas a night. He'd offered to drive me to Oklahoma City no matter how late it was, I want you to get your money's worth, he kept saying about my time on the tour, but I was trying to be firm, no it's too late, can I stay over? He'd said of course you can, but I think I should drive you. We'd left it at that because I had to get on the plane.

Now, I was tired and hardly listening to him. I was following him around his house while he folded some towels out of the laundry.

My whole life Hank has had this green-and-white watercolor in his house with some deep pencil lines across what looks like a tub. I've always liked it. I was looking at it now while he talked. He was saying something about this period in my childhood where he'd had my brothers and I'd gone with my mom. She and I moved into this guy's house in California and it was violent. Hank knew the guy had a drug problem and was awful and I wanted to come get you, he'd said. Nobody was doing anything and you were stuck there, but I was afraid that if I came and got you, it would be considered kidnapping and I'd lose the boys.

I tried to remember the last time I'd been there. I couldn't really remember. Topo Chicos in all their forms were everywhere, the boxes, the bottles, the bigger bottles.

My favorite thing in the house is the naked box spring and mattress in the dining room with stuff piled all around it, including a professional portrait of Hank, Mom, Tye, Gunner, and me that we'd done when I was sixteen. The photo was still there. We all wore white shirts, it had a white background and a light wooden frame. We were cute actually. It was on the floor, leaning up against the mattress. We had gotten the photo taken when Mom and Hank were trying to reconcile—this was the last attempt. I'd been very angry that we were all in the same room for any reason. It was the most fake thing to be taking the photo, I'd felt. My hair hangs in my face.

Hank had been saying kidnapping.

Gunner was in the other room typing and talking into a headset. Tye was in the living room doing the exact same thing on a larger computer. They were playing together.

Night looks so good in Dallas somehow, a heavy heat saves itself.

Hank was connecting with me.

This was their current house. The boys were in their twenties. Everyone living together still. Loving each other. I'd been in and out of their lives since I was six, mostly out, but for two years in high school I'd lived with them. We said nothing to each other.

It was May and already too hot for me. I'd just bought a brown cowboy hat to impress everyone back in California because suddenly this was cool. I hadn't been to Dallas in the summer since high school. I was thirty-one now.

Hank was talking and my shoulder blades were real near each other. The boys made their sounds in the other room.

Hank was looking at me like, you know? He was telling me this story and I was looking at the painting. The lines that leaked into the corners excited me most. I looked at it and listened to him. Was that a bush poking out of the tub and a leg? I'd looked at these lines for years and suddenly, while I was looking and listening, they were forming a nude. Was it a body in a tub? I'd never seen it.

When Hank had picked me up from the airport earlier that night, he had Gunner in the car and some blankets and some fruit and was ready to drive me to Oklahoma. He was like, get in we're going. And I was like, nope. I told you I really want to stay with you for the night and he looked at me in the rearview mirror for a long time without moving.

So you're a man now, Hank said once he relented and started driving us to his house. He wasn't smiling. You can take care of yourself, huh?

He was in a hoodie and looked so soft as he said this. I watched his hands on the steering wheel, they were padded and warm.

He hadn't really known that I'd pinned myself to boyhood with Jo, but he could probably feel it. How do I enter maturity? I don't want to use his version of man-ness to get in, woman-ness either.

Gunner watched this scene between Hank and me. We hadn't seen each other in a while. I wanted to ask him hundreds of things. It was raining and Hank was looking at me in the rearview mirror and turning around on the parkways. I said I don't even know what that means. Gunner glanced up and then looked at his feet.

DADDY BOY

Yesterday, I finished this Netflix series about the Snoop Youth Football League and one of the kids was being raised by his young grandpa who looked so much like Hank. Probably a Taurus, wearing sweatshirts and driving a clean truck and telling the kid not to wear slippers to school and sort of grumbling. The man seemed to love grumbling and seemed to love caring for this kid.

Before Hank built me a room in his house in Dallas when I was a teenager, I stayed on the top bunk in Tye and Gunner's room. Hank didn't sleep anywhere, the couch maybe? The dog had eaten a hole in the bathroom door and I'd written this thing about the act of loving being kind on the bedroom wall in chalk.

I was trying to find my place. I'd clean for them: black trash bags everywhere.

Nobody ever went to sleep. There was always something on. Did I have a toothbrush? Where did I put my shoes? I'd eventually hide drugs in a tampon box because no one would ever look in there.

Hank came up to the bunk bed to give me a towel one night. He was putting on a shirt and his hair was wet. I'd been listening to Tye and Gunner play Madden. The dog was big and looking for Hank. He'd just taken us to the Gap outlet and I'd gotten a new backpack that matched the boys' and a red zip-up hoodie that I wore every day after that.

He hung my backpack on the doorknob for me.

I love you, he'd said. Don't forget to take it all as entertainment.

And he meant my mom and all that had happened that led me to that bunk.

I'd loved my room there so much. Hank had framed up a small porch that had been on the back of the house and sheet-rocked it himself. He'd put in a door that had this blue-tinted glass and slid. He'd done it himself to make room for me. When he finally finished and showed it to me, I felt like I was in one of those car commercials where there'd be a bow on a car. I'd slide open that door and lie in my bed and look at the ceiling that I'd painted Superman Blue.

But by the time I was sixteen, nobody lived there anymore. Not Hank, not Gunner, not Tye. Everything had ended and everyone was gone. Hank was letting Mom back into his life. I wasn't able to be part of this life, my new living situation had been recently negotiated by Child Protective Services and I was supposed to be living at Hank's, so when they left that house and shut it down, I had to just leave and go nowhere. On nights where I wasn't sleeping at the church or at some random dude's house, I'd break back in. I'd crawl in through the window that Hank had framed in there for me. The floors made so much noise. There was a condemned notice—or a notice of no occupancy, or something official that I never actually read—on the front door and the windows were broken, but my bed was still there. I'd covered it in plastic that I'd found to prevent bugs from getting in. I would put a bottle in my pants pocket and climb this little tree to the open kitchen window and then go to my room. Everything smelled like weed because I was squatting in my own house, sleeping there, and that was all I had going on. No one would ever go back, just me.

I lay in there and looked at the ceiling.

I'd loved that Orlando trip.

Hank remembers me watching the Discovery Channel storm chasing shows on loop in high school. TLC had a few too. When I decided I was going chasing that May, and I told him about it, he thought I was finally doing the things I'd always wanted to do, like a retiree.

I often wonder what I had wanted back then, when I was watching all those shows. I guess any hobby just gets to be a hobby. Like I said to Derek, I could have been a horse girl/boy or something just the same and been obsessed with that, but I wasn't. I wanted weather. Maybe I wanted to be put in my place. Maybe I wanted everyone put in theirs.

Honestly, for all my trying, I've only actually seen a tornado twice. The first time, I was eleven and Mom, Hank, Gunner and Tye, and I were in a rented place in Glen Rose that had a cowboy pool—a giant cistern filled with farm water. I'd been playing in that pool and then this storm started up. Hank had taken Tye to the store or something. Mom and Gunner were watching *Bambi* in the rental. I remember seeing the deer looking around for its mother on the screen, a small early '90s TV with the VHS component baked in. The deer couldn't find its mother because she'd just been killed. Hank and Tye were still gone when the sirens started. The sound pealed up from the ravine below. This was one of the happiest times we'd had—Hank, Tye, Gunner, Mom, and me. I remember seeing the virga, and starting to notice the base of the cloud beginning to rotate.

I was watching this whole thing happen like thirty yards away and I told Mom it was time to get to the bathroom. She went with Gunner, and I stood on the back porch watching. I wasn't watching for Hank. I was hoping there'd be a funnel that I'd get to be part of. I wanted to be absorbed into the green that was purpling. That very specific color that only some people know. It was looking so soft. The sky literally came over, it came down and over, it was sweeping up anything loose, leaves, pieces of trash, and moving everything toward itself. I wanted to go too. I was disappointed when the tornado didn't touch down. I never joined them in the bathroom. The funnel popped back up and then Glen Rose got several minutes of hail.

DADDY BOY

As I write this, in my little East Coast town, it's raining, but in a weird way, there's nothing on the radar, no green blob that indicates rain (I look at the radar on my phone all the time). I've been googling around. Radar works like this: radio waves are sent out and hit against "objects" like ice in the atmosphere and that's what we see as colors on the radar. "The larger the object, the greater the amount of energy that is returned to the radar."

This process also registers time and direction, according to the National Oceanic and Atmospheric Association. Something's not working in this moment, though, I guess. Right now I'm pretty sure it's raining. The radar disagrees, its current status is a sun ball. Everyone has umbrellas out and they're running. I love this failure.

It makes me think about powerlessness.

Recently, I watched a CGI version of the *Titanic* sinking in real time. It's a two-hour-and-forty-one-minute YouTube video. No one would watch it with me. I made popcorn for myself and sat in my desk chair. I wanted to watch the sea eat the thing.

As a general rule, I'm terrorized and excited to the point of jubilance about shipwrecks. I get a tingle at the back of my neck and the place where my ass meets my thigh whenever I think about it—seawater where it's not supposed to be, a boat where it's not supposed to be.

My grandparents have always told me, the sea gives and the sea takes away, looking wistfully off when they say it. When I was a kid, I swam over what I was told was a sunken ship and thought my feet could kick the mast—I could see a mast, couldn't really kick it, could see that it was collecting seaweed and seagrass and rotting there with paint chipping off. It looked like a finger. I was horrified and happy, swimming around with a well in my stomach, a smiling horror. At home, I have books like *Sea Sense* on my bookshelf and curled pictures of boats. I tell everyone that the thought of dying at sea is comforting to me, terrifying and sweet.

I watched the CGI *Titanic* go through all its stages of sinking, watching as each little computer-generated portal fell below the waterline. When it was nearly submerged, the video took its viewer on a tour of the inside cabins with fake water filling up, furniture sloshing over, swamping paintings and books.

The moral of the Titanic story has remained *try and beat the sea, you can't*. The puritan version of this is, don't brag so much. An unknown Titanic crew member is reported to have said to embarking passenger Mrs. Sylvia Caldwell: "God himself could not sink this ship!"

I don't care about this puritan version, though—I'm interested in the taming the sea one, our instinct to make it safer, to win. The lore of the *Titanic* says, ultimately, painfully, that the sea will always be unfathomable.

Last week, I finished this book called *The Power of the Sea* about tsunamis, storm surges, rogue waves. In it, the author, Bruce Parker, looks to the last few lines of Rachel Carson's *The Sea Around Us*. "Even with all our modern instruments for probing and sampling the deep ocean," Carson writes, "no one can say that we shall ever resolve the last, the ultimate mysteries of the sea." Parker takes offense to this, and suggests that Carson's statement "was made... as a way to extol the sea's grandeur, that grandeur keeping the sea from being totally understood." He argues instead that with our "growing Global Ocean Observing System and our ever-improving dynamic computer models" we're going to solve all the mysteries and be good to go. I hate the idea, honestly. I'm so tired of the idea that we can know it all, capture it, figure it out, this framework exhausts me.

"What is it to surrender to the capacity to think?" writes Donna J. Haraway in *Staying with the Trouble*.

My favorite weather memories are power outages where we all would have to sit in the same room, in front of the wood stove, and look at each other. The people in my life who never stopped were stalled. The people who lived with their backs to me were very suddenly facing me.

I remember my biological dad and I once playing with a Lite-Brite during a power outage. He was somewhere behind me and I was making those colored lights into a dog or something and then the power was out and he was suddenly there. I saw him infrequently after he and my mom split, but I do remember this little weather book he had for me. It was a board book with a person in a sou'wester on it and you could press this red button and the dude would say, "looks like we're in for some weather." We read that together in the dark.

Do you get what I'm saying?

I fell in love with this feeling.

I was pacing outside that Oklahoma City airport bus stop. It was so extremely sunny. The sun was bouncing off all the yellow curbs. I was pretty much alone, which I enjoy always. It had been a long morning. Hank hadn't been able to drive me, which is why he'd been so adamant to do it the night before, so Tye had given me a ride to Love Field, where I'd rented a car and driven myself. I was glad to be doing it. Things were quiet because it was that magic 10 a.m. or 11 a.m. period when you're in a public space and it seems to only be you. This is my favorite time of day to do anything. I stood there waiting, trying to fix my sunglasses that had twisted out of shape. I was about to be in a very concentrated space with people. I'd missed the first night with them and I imagined that their bonding was bad for me.

While we were on the road, I realized I didn't really want Tye to drop me off. I'd started thinking that if I really wanted to connect with my family why not just stay with them? Except this is what always happens, a day or two in—we all get together and they start laughing. Is it teasing? The worst part isn't feeling disliked. It's the feeling of wanting to be liked. I question whether or not I am hearing things right. I get brisk and blunt and angry and then end up feeling guilty when Hank says things like, come on, everything's fine. As I've aged, this whole paradigm feels unsurvivable. Did I want some strangers in a van to be their surrogates?

I wasn't with Tye or Gunner for much of our childhood. I missed a lot of their bonding and what they bonded over were things I didn't care about at all or wasn't invited to care about anyway. Maybe this is a book about giving up.

When Tye dropped me off, I tried to untangle a set of headphones that were balled up in my pocket. I tried to do it with my one hand, which we all know is futile. I hope you have a great time, he was saying, not looking in my eyes because he doesn't usually. I love you, he said, though, very seriously. I thought of trying to hug him through the car. He said I love you again and then pulled out of the sun-soaked rental lot and headed to wherever he was working at the time.

Goddamn, to be him, you know?

Before I left, I took a selfie with a timer in his apartment. It had just rained, so when I took the photo there were still raindrops on my shoulders from being outside. I had my Stetson on and my hands in the pockets of my overalls. He didn't see me take it. I wouldn't have wanted him to. I look like a tourist but I'm not, my want is to know him and Gunner and to celebrate the whole experience of that atmosphere: Dallas is so, so real.

Something in me keeps trying to connect. But you know, sometimes there's just a cloud and every once in a while, there's the exact conditions for a storm. What turns a grass-hopper into a locust?

In my mind, I've deleted that we're only half siblings. I just deleted it. I haven't experienced any other kinds of siblings, so I don't know the difference. Tye and Gunner know the difference though. Even on a recent call to Tye, we'd just been talking about things and he was like, well don't feel like you're missing out, the Ross side is just the same, using their last name, like, I don't know how much you know about how this side of the family works but... and I was like, damn. Blood has meant so much to Hank, being his blood, but I don't share it. The hurt of this gap is so loud. It also is so permanent.

I'm on T right now and sometimes I catch my own eyes in a mirror and I look like Gunner. My hair is the same as his and I see us in there. I don't think he'd agree. I've had to get all new pants. I don't know how this is going to go. Does the testos-terone accrue in my body and like transition me? I'm on the low dose, the kind that wasn't available to us when I was first wanting to do it. I'm on the squirt of gel per day and I'd happily be on it for the rest of my life, but what does that do and does anybody actually know? Like do I start passing when the T has grown and grown in my system or is this more like what would happen if I swallowed a fish and it lived swimming in my system, but I never start being a fish?

When I got that fifty-dollars-per-day Kia Rio from Love Field and aimed it toward the Oklahoma City Airport, I picked a Petey Pablo playlist to remind myself of storm chasing with those people off of AOL. I headed in that direction where roads are flat forever, tires screaming across arbitrary state lines, toward all the stolen names for places. What kind of murder does naming do? There are bluebonnets everywhere— named after settler women's hats—waving along the highway. They're a type of lupin that was domesticated in Egypt in the twenty-second century BC. Peruvians cultivated them, too, which is probably why this genus is waving around Texas, but nobody talks about that.

When I pulled up to the Oklahoma City airport car rental lot where I was going to meet the tour, the heat was enormous. What bug makes that sound in the heat? The tinnitus-like one. Do you know it? Like a fridge running.

I remember reading *The Stranger* in high school and thinking of the beach like a parking lot and how that guy just shot someone because of how blinding the sun was and how hot he was and how much I understood that. White heat coming off the asphalt wrecks me. I dropped off the car and put the keys in a box next to an old ashtray fixed to the white stucco wall like I was supposed to. My sunglasses and their loose screws worried me and I stood there trying to screw them in with my fingers. I was told to wait by the front and they'd come get me. They pulled up quickly. They'd seen me.

The door opened and even though I knew it would open, I was surprised. The van was packed with people and they scooted over to make me a spot in the second row, which seemed good. A guy in a neon yellow Storm Travelers T-shirt, this was Derek, got out and walked over to me, took my bag.

That's great! he said. We found you.

I stepped toward the van and a guy my height bounced out to invite me in.

Derek got back in beside the driver. The two of them looked like my brothers, like they'd been on a computer for days—a slight heat smell, hot shirts.

Hank's cars always smelled so good to me. They were always so big. He had a lot of clothes in the back for whatever reason and tools, like all kinds of them, and plans in rolls everywhere. He had this one shirt that we made fun of so much, his fish shirt with orange tropical fish on a blue background that was often hanging on one of those plastic clothes hooks in the way back. His work was filleted in there. Just wide open.

What storm chasing reminded me of most was a church trip, not exactly that mission trip kind, but the smaller weird weekend ones where you'd go to a cabin in east Texas and someone would wash your feet symbolically in a Tupperware bucket: desperate adults moved together.

Now, I was sitting in that second row and all the other passengers were settled around me like nightfall.

The space between the two captain's seats was filled with open bags, sweatshirts, a suitcase of snacks. There was a swivel stand with a computer on it, spun around and toward us. Plastic bags have a particular twisting: jerky seems the same as plastic. Few feet were on the ground. I had crumpled flowers in my bag but they didn't know that. The visors in the front were clipped with sunglass cases and other soft storage. There was an orange owl, a bobblehead with big puppy eyes and plastic wings, bopping on the dashboard.

There were three rows, all gray fabric.

Are you okay with cunt?

This guy who had let me in was asking.

He meant the word. Everyone looked ready for laughter. There was not one cloud.

I learned quickly that all of the passengers were from Essex or close to Essex. I waited for another accent while we did our intros and none came. They were friendly and told me nearly in unison that there was no weather in the UK like this—none that was severe, and so they do this each season. All of them besides one had been on numerous tours with Storm Travelers, like five or more. None of them had ever met because Storm Travelers did a number of tours each year and it was possible to meet new people like this each time, that was part of the draw for them, apparently.

I liked how each of them smiled. The emphasis was on their chins. We were about to be all together. The crew from Essex was probably attracted to storm chasing tours because they've been covered in UK media outlets. One of the articles quotes a company saying that their trip "captures the romantic notions of the American West—the freedom of movement, wandering the Plains in endless pursuit of the horizon..."

Here's the "American West":

Just out of curiosity, I would like to know if any chasers have had their cars searched in the past? wrote a storm chaser on StormTrack. The poster was born and raised in the plains, described themselves as Brown and said they were stopped often when trying to chase. He was asking what other people do. The consensus seemed to be stay the fuck away from "middle America" to be safe. But I'm from here, the guy kept responding.

Derek was adjusting his rearview mirror and sitting back down, he'd said, you ready for a tour of genocide? Of manifest destiny and murder? Moz, the same guy asking about cunt, was sitting forward in his seat. He had a slight scruff and was in a thick sweatshirt. He wore black shorts that were cut off at the most contemporary leg spot for men's fashion. He was in music he said. He told a story about talking to a bunch of German Nazis in a pub in London who were wearing swastika hoodies—the Hindu Sanskrit symbol of good luck, he'd said, those demons stole it. I'm Punjabi, he'd nodded, American Nazis seem boring compared to German ones.

A guy in the way back laughed. I don't know, he'd said. This guy, Jamal, was sitting directly behind Moz in a striped shirt and smelled like he'd just shaved, he smiled with his whole face, said he'd just been to North Korea.

I'm in risk management, he nodded, I'm interested in euphoria.

We slowed to go over a speed bump that was placed in the middle of a very dry-looking town.

The plateaus were showing up. Everyone seemed to giggle about the bump. I giggled to participate. I am always only half listening, though, because I'm always writing—mediated reality is what autobiography is, I heard Maggie Nelson say once. Always, the hum of internal commentary. I took notes. I looked around the van. I wondered about responsibility.

I watched Derek look at us all in his rearview mirror.

I am thinking of standing on an outdoor train platform with ivy along the concrete, I guess this was in Brooklyn. The light was early fall. A crowd was trying to get a person off the tracks, he had been standing down there. Someone shouted about him being drunk and just pick him up, and four people carried him and set him to the side. All of them had decided they were responsible.

Now, in the van, we'd come together like that: as randomly as people on a platform.

It was odd because I had sort of pictured the tour this way and I also hadn't. I think I'd figured I'd feel more alone. I'd known about the whole swath of people in white vans wetting the road during tornado season and paying to be there. I knew that (more or less) experienced meteorologists would pair up with drivers and take the white vans full of people around. I wondered why they'd pay four thousand dollars per spot to be one of like seven, I guess I figured these people were all bros, like the people who cliff jump in those flying squirrel suits. I figured they were moneyed. I also assumed they were from Colorado or Nevada. I'd pictured people with very different accents than these ones. I hadn't thought of it as an international activity, but apparently, no matter the season (late spring to early summer), these tours are packed with British people. Like many people, we'd all been influenced by the movie *Twister*, and then the infinite-seeming shows about tornado chasers, which led to this, white people in cargo shorts running around holding handi-cams and breathing hard. Sometimes they're bleeding because they got too close to the debris. There's money in it, too, even just from YouTube views, like Derek had said. These YouTube view tourists often orient themselves around the science, and, like Helen Hunt, avenging things. The avenging-the-past version of storm chasing often thinks of itself as saving lives: to this day, sometimes the only way the sirens get turned on in all these towns and cities is because a human sees the tornado touch down and calls it in. But this group didn't feel like that, maybe because everyone was just smiling.

Chronos is the father of Zeus, Jamal was saying behind me. So that means time is the birthplace of weather.

I had had my headphones in, but took them out when I heard Zeus.

It was so sunny and we seemed to have an enormous amount of time.

This was day one.

People have died, Derek was saying. The owl on the dashboard bobbed.

It took all the joy out to learn about the deaths, Tony, the guy driving, said.

We were passing the Twistex Memorial in El Reno.

It's a plaque like a war memorial along the highway in Oklahoma that's dedicated to Tim Samaras, Carl Young, and Paul Samaras. The tornado was on May 31, 2013. If you watched *Storm Chasers* you know that these were the science guys and they seemed the most focused on safety. It was shocking that they'd died in the tornado. Way more shocking than it would be for anyone else to have, in some ways. They were a father and son team.

I'd watched videos about the El Reno tornado before, many actually. I think there's a tornado on the ground but I can't see it, chasers in the videos say.

From the front seat, Derek and Tony were talking about another tour company, this one called Excellent Tornado Tours, going into Moore, Oklahoma, the site of two of the deadliest tornadoes ever recorded, with a "wrap"—a festive advertisement that wraps around the van—and getting emails with death threats.

I'd started in with questions about how weird is it that we're going on a tour to look at destruction. I wasn't trying to make friends. I was thinking of all the British people in the vans and how maybe most of these folks had no stake in what happened out here and who was blown away besides a sort of sour feeling. So now we take our magnets off when we go into Joplin, Derek said. The trees in Joplin were debarked, he continued.

DADDY BOY

The Joplin, Missouri, tornado was in 2011 and had worst-case-scenario timing. It hit the town as the schools were letting out for the day and killed 160 people.

People die all the time in NASCAR and everyone's still watching, Tony said, reaching for a condensation-warped Wendy's soda in his cup holder.

By afternoon, the squares of sun on my legs itched. I'd only been in the van for a couple of hours. My legs were cramped and I wanted to take off my shoes—all this sitting made me want to nap. I wasn't expecting these ecstatic people, checking weather apps and radars and sharing about it all the time, excited to look at 330 bars and convective outlooks in Essex accents. Derek seemed so happy, he was inflated with happiness and everyone was matching him with their chests up, their cameras out.

I make it work, Derek had said to me by email when we were discussing money. It was essential that he pulled this off. It became clear at some point that he made all his income over these few months and he really needed this to go well.

I'm not going to let you down, he was saying to us all.

It seemed impossible to let these folks down because they were so content—the first people I'd ever been around who were delighted to read the Cloud Appreciation Society website together.

As a kid, I'd memorized the 1999 edition of *Peterson First Guide to Clouds and Weather*. The inscription on the one I have says, "May your clouds watching always be happy, grandmother and granddaddy."

I don't know why Hank's parents gave me a cloud book. I was seven and in response to the gift, I started a club with Gunner only. I called it "rain check" and I'd make him come with me out to the sidewalk in his diaper in Sacramento with a magnifying glass to look for evidence of rain. There never was any.

I didn't know Hank's parents well. I'd been to their house in Amarillo only a handful of times over the years. They used to ask me the whole thing about why is there a hole in Texas Stadium? So God can watch his favorite team, is what we were supposed to say. I don't think of them as religious. I remember hearing about them spray-painting tumbleweeds to make a Christmas tree or a snowman. They had a huge pool table.

Whenever we'd visit them, we'd always go do something in a field: make paper airplanes, play cards, eat bologna. I don't like being in fields.

The last time I was in Amarillo, I'd gone with Hank and his brother to their burial plot. It was Hank's first time seeing it. While we were there, we saw one of the chuck wagon breakfast tourist things in the Palo Duro Canyon: dried water and dust, blonde Texas. Hank explained that a tour group pulls chuck wagons out into the desert, some big money stuff, he'd joked. They take paying customers into the canyon on horseback and feed them breakfast casserole, brisket, beans, and other "cowboy" things. We walked behind the tour for a while, the tin cups clinking that people would eat beans out of when the wagon stopped in the ravine. The topography looked like Hank, his eyes ran with it. He always tells stories about having a hard time with any other colors, he lived in New York City for a while and really struggled with the green/black, he'd said. He likes yellow/brown.

His parents, Bevo and Bull, are buried now in the cemetery right near that canyon, with black marble plaques nestled into a shrubby highland. It's all surrounded by a red-metal cow fence with the red kind of swinging gate. The cemetery is next to this place where Hank's brother likes to get his meat. We stood with the bags of meat looking at the graves. Hank's brother had made a hard, faux marble sticker for Grandad's plaque: "My last words were, my balls are on fire" it said. He stuck it under the etched "Bull" and we stood in silence. I watched the weight of the meat in his plastic bag make the bag swing.

I was honored they'd let me join.

In Hank's bedroom in Dallas he's got a big black-and-white portrait that Mom took. It's framed and propped up on his dresser. In it, he's standing still with his hands in his pockets. Gunner is half twirling and Tye is sort of marching. It is a portrait of Texas.

I'm somewhere with Mom—we're out of the frame.

They're on a dusty cobblestone street in the center of an old town—Hico. It's only about eighteen minutes from Dublin and is home to the museum of Billy the Kid, a.k.a. William Bonney, who was infamous for being a "bad boy." He'd escaped a scheduled hanging and became known for that in 1880 or so. Everything refers to him (as is typical in US descriptions of European and settler-descended "outlaws") as "baby-faced."

I had to look this up for you because honestly I don't know why Billy is cared about. Somebody asked on Quora why Billy the Kid is idolized and an anonymous poster wrote, "For the same reason a barbarian like Alexander the Great is. There was nothing great about him... Billy the Kid is just one of many outlaws (criminals) that whites have privileged themselves to deify."

We never went to the museum. We were actually in Hico for its Dr. Pepper plant, the oldest bottling facility in the state of Texas, apparently, and our whole goal was to go there and get cane sugar Dr. Pepper versus the kind with high-fructose corn syrup. Not because we cared about health effects, just because it was novel and good.

I only even registered the Billy the Kid Museum at all because in one of my Texas history classes (Texas history, as well as saying the Texas pledge in the morning, was an integral part of my schooling), we 'd read a book that described Billy as "small and girlish looking."

Michael Ondaatje's *The Collected Works of Billy the Kid* seems to play with this depiction. Ondaatje has invented this whole identity for Billy and made him sort of queer amid descriptions of the plains, of grasses and horses and the texture of that.

Why did Ondaatje care about Billy, is something I've wondered— maybe he's toying with Emmett Dalton's assessment that Billy "symbolizes the undying anarchy in the heart of every man," or what writer Stephen Tatum said in a 1941 *Life* magazine piece that Billy's a "flexible container."

The whole thing is that Billy wanted to avenge his employer's murder. He'd decided to respond, and the decision became a promise. Is there such a thing as disappointment without promise?

One of Hank's greatest lines from our childhood was, potential is what gets you fired. He'd say it all the time about sports and anything else, like you have to keep your word, you have to match your promise with results.

What if it's not in your power? I'd say.

Well, then you'd better figure out how to make it be, he'd joke.

"Billy the Kid would come in often / and sometimes stayed for a week or two. / I remember how frightened I was the first time he came," writes Ondaatje.

Hank has three brothers and, growing up, they'd tear into each other. All they ever reminisce about now are beatings and parasailing with homemade sails tied to the tailgates of Cadillacs. I got to live near Hank's brother when I lived in LA and we'd hang out in his neighborhood and he'd drink Modelos and explain how they're Muscogee (Creek) and Scottish men and they've always had to prove themselves.

Recently, I got this book with a pink sunset on it. It's a workbook for "Mindful Masculinities," edited by Rocco Kayiatos.

Nobody knows what masculinity is anyway, the book keeps saying. There's a movement of people, like Jack Halberstam, who add an *s* on the end to say there's so many masculinities! And aren't we absurd to assume only cis men contribute to it—all ideal masculinity by its very nature is just out of reach, writes Halberstam in *The Queer Art of Failure*.

At one point, I wrote you a whole book about embodying femininity, like, what is it? What if it could exist outside of a white cis-male conception of woman-ness, like, what if it's somewhere else and something totally other than "woman?" As of yet, femininity has been defined so exclusively as the opposite of masculinity—which, in turn, shores up the position of "man."

I was happy to read this part of Kayiatos's workbook, from an essay by Mike Sagun:

"To my mind, the trouble arises when we conflate masculinity and femininity with gender, as such when we're actually speaking about energies."

I was reading this right after signing up for Folx, a service that'll deliver hormones (expensive ones) to your house without an outside doctor's appointment or insurance. It was three in the morning and I couldn't sleep and I signed up in this way that felt like crossing my arms over my chest. A surrender to my own desire is what I'm describing.

I have a student who specializes in hormones and epigenetics, and is studying how hormones are such a complex system having to do with gut microbiota and literally everything else. We spoke yesterday about her work and she essentially said that play is the only real answer. That why shouldn't we get to play with the hormones in our bodies? Because, think about it: so many cis people are on hormones of all kinds. Like there are synthetic hormones everywhere, in our water, our food... let's be curious and have some goddamn fun, she was saying—she'd lit up.

• • •

I wasn't fully prepared for this scene: Derek had a little orange pill bottle that he was reaching into for communion wafers. This is the church of convection (a meteorology joke), he was saying. Want one? He passed it to me.

This is so southern, I realize, but Derek was from New Jersey.

This was his way of saying hello. He had one leg out of the open passenger side door and was chatting and hanging onto the handle with his free arm. Everyone wanted to talk to Derek, people at the gas station, strangers, other chasers. Everybody.

No one seemed to want to talk to Tony, who was from Iowa and looked like everyone in the videos, like literally all the drivers in the videos, with gray T-shirts and fluffy hair and a Big Gulp and who are somewhat submissive because they're paid to take instructions while others watch all day.

Moz was in the van going through his camera equipment, he was calm and kept his arms crossed a lot of the time, but it was clear he was on the balls of his feet because he's talented at taking these photos. He'd shown me his Instagram.

Samuel was someone I didn't know and figured I'd never get to know. He was walking back from the 7-Eleven with a Sprite. He didn't say much to anyone and stepped back into the van, sliding over to the spot that was mostly in shadow. He tended to sit in the shadow wearing super white sneakers.

DADDY BOY

June was taking selfies while Jamal ate wafers with Derek. June was wearing pink camo, her bags were all pink camo, too, she was in the British army or something. She had a pink selfie stick that was not camo.

There's no shame about selfies here.

This was sort of the pattern: everyone out, everyone back in again. When Samuel got in the van, we all followed in a meandering way. Tony finished pumping gas and I got in next to Moz. Jamal and Derek stopped playing around and we started off toward somewhere. This was a significant thing I hadn't realized: we were just going to go. That was the point of the van, to be dexterous. We might drive for five states, we might drive into Mexico, we might go east. We just had to see. It was late afternoon and we were heading toward indistinct brush on a thin dirt road. I don't know why, but I thought we'd immediately and easily find a storm.

I was wearing a T-shirt and ripped black shorts, my toes made more sweat in my rubber shoes, there was a sugar smell in my hair. The AC blew dimples into everyone's clothes. I assumed bad weather was everywhere.

All of us would like to find ourselves subordinate, fucked, actually, by a storm—or maybe that's just me and all they wanted was a cowboy thing, capture weather on camera and go viral, live through the internet that way.

Look, look, Jamal was saying and showing his Instagram to everybody because there'd been a waterspout back in the UK. It was churning through the Thames, or at least, that's where I'd imagined it, whisking hats off of old men and taking people's rose gardens with it.

Nothing was happening here.

I guess we're waiting, June said.

She didn't say a whole lot, so this felt resounding.

Surrender doesn't happen on our time.

I'd started to do the reporter thing where I was leaning forward and asking everybody questions.

My favorite thing to do is to be a reporter in all social situations. It's because that kind of dynamic of observer and observed is more comfortable for me. I'm more confident socially if I've already removed myself.

Derek was saying, okay everybody, we're running into some trouble, but we're going to make it as fun as possible.

Everyone stopped clicking around on their cameras and looked up at him.

DADDY BOY

He was suddenly holding the van by the neck like a leaking balloon.

We're in for a stretch of fair weather, Derek said.

Jo used to tell this story about how the little black Keds I wore all summer smelled so bad that she used to make me put them by the mailboxes and walk the four floors in my socks.

I remember buying extreme men's bodega gel deodorant to rub inside those Keds before I went over to her place. It didn't make a difference. I'd squish around.

We were once standing together below this undulating mammatus sky. Do you know what that is? It's when the clouds look like they're bubbling. They're named after mammaries. My friends Nai and Ryan were there too—we were all in Chelsea and it was really my first time. Ryan was holding a handmade sign that said hate crimes are heart-breaking. Jo had a top hat with a green sticker that said fuck your gender on it. I had something on that she'd loaned me, a mesh shirt and makeup.

Those mammatus clouds came out and turned everything pink. Everyone was gold. We were screaming about STAR and how the Stonewall memorial was absurd: two white gay couples holding each other in the park. Those clouds often

come after rain. Here's what it is: I was born right then.
Timing is everything I guess. I was feral. I don't know that
I like that language but that's what people said I was. I ate
my own hand. I'd missed learning everything. I didn't know
to brush my teeth. I didn't eat or understand eating. But I
had figured out the subway. I had about $3 a day to spend on
things in total.

Jo would say, I'm making salad, want some? and I'd say, I'm
around the corner when I was really in Brooklyn, and we'd
walk around the city looking for the moon. We'd smoke rolled
cigarettes with our chins tilted up, my reporter's notebook
always flapping, pages constantly trying to escape my pocket.
New York was an enormous night, still is.

The first time I went over to her apartment, it was because she
needed somebody to watch her cat. I went over while she was
getting ready to go work, she had this wooden cabinet by the
door filled with equipment. She was pulling out implements
and talking to me about what I needed to do with the cat. I
stuffed my hands in my pockets, listening, trying to be cool.

She pulled a silver funnel-looking thing out of the closet and
put it in her bag.

What's that?

DADDY BOY

Piss play, she said.

I raised my eyebrows. Cool, I said.

I was on EBT but was out of it. She didn't have much in her cupboards, but while she was gone, I ate an entire box of old Medjool dates that were on a shelf above the fridge, an entire jar of coconut oil.

Holy shit, she said, holding the jar when she got home. You must have been giving a lot of massages.

Massages?

That's what I use this for. I ate it, I said.

Oh my god. She doubled over laughing. This was before all these people were swishing it around in their mouths. She put her hands on her knees.

I was hungry!

I'm sorry I'm laughing, she said. You're adorable.

I first met Jo when a leak sprung in the plumbing at my job, where I was an assistant building manager. When I'd walked into our four-story building in SoHo, it had been dripping so long it felt like a rainforest, steam coming off the carpet. She was the one who'd discovered the leak (she volunteered there) and I had to watch footage of her finding it for hours and hours. I had to interview her about what she'd found, watch footage of her discovering the puddle on the second floor thousands of times. She was wearing a green tank top. I was wearing a black jean jacket that said MTV on the back. We struck up a conversation then and I kept it up.

I want to explain how I was at the time: I wanted something that had always looked so good. Was it care?

Jo let me look up at her like the "please sir" emoji. (The eyes up watering one. Try typing it in if you haven't on an iPhone and you'll get that emoji as a suggestion, doesn't work with "please ma'am" or anything else.) She responded with a softness. I'd hit my head on the wall and she'd stop me, saying something like, I'm not going anywhere, which made me feel amazing.

I shocked myself when I walked away from this.

Recently, I listened to Fred Moten lecturing about maturity, he was talking about a student he's working with who's studying Peter Pan. Fred is saying that country music and blues music is replete with *somebody call my mama* and *I never should have left home*. "Normal" development: there's an exile involved in it, Moten's saying.

Hank said he'd been talking about me to my brothers lately

and was saying, well Em has been on his own since he was sixteen, and then corrected himself and said, forever really, Em has been on his own. Can I go on this exile that's required of "normal development" if I've never been anywhere? If home has been so distant? I think of Tye and Gunner who live still very close to each other and in Dallas. They're seen as adult men. I've been on the road forever and I compare myself.

I think a lot about reparenting these days. How do I do it to myself? All of us are talking about it, it's like the new astrology.

I saw a cartoon just today by a person named Brainbooger who had posted a couple panels on Instagram: "I wish I knew more transgender elders," the first piece said. "I wish more of us got to grow old." The image to accompany it was a person with long wavy hair and a slight frown. The next slide had an image of the same person using an Instagram age filter that gave them puffy cheeks and wrinkles. "It's hard to imagine myself aging," it said, "Not a lot of role models, I guess."

The most active trans group in my area has some activities for elders, which it defines as anyone over thirty-five. My friend and I laugh about this a lot because we're both thirty-five but it's not funny.

An elder is like a map.

Right now, I live with three dogs who I love and sometimes people are like, oh your daddy dropped your leash, or sometimes your mommy loves you, things like that and they mean me.

I've tried to traipse behind Miss Major Griffin-Gracy for most of my adult life. Have you seen her film *Major!*?

At one point in the film, Miss Major is wearing one of those giftshop T-shirts that says BEST DAD with rainbow kid handprints and her son shows up in the film to help her commemorate a building being named after her in New York. He's the best dad, says Christopher, her son.

When I've shown *Major!* in class, my students freeze at this scene because they think she's being misgendered, but a person quoted in the film says that Miss Major is truly gender-queer in that way, like, she gets to be everything. The next scene in the film is her saying that she'd been kicked out of a group for single parents because she was a dad with breasts. She laughs at the idea.

When I show it to my students, I always combine the viewing with Tourmaline's short animated film about Miss Major, *The Personal Things*, it's beautiful, shows Major with black and white hair flowing on a long sectional couch.

In it, Major talks about changing all her documents back to male, saying, "it dawned on me, wait a minute, I don't feel female, I want everybody to know I am a transgender person and love me for that. Fuck this other stuff. So I changed all my stuff back to male, that was my way to strike back."

In the film, she doesn't give her exact age, but hints at being born around 1940. That would mean that she's changing her identity documents as a seventy-five-or-so year old: she's been a dad and a mother and a grandmother and she's walking all the time through this revolving door.

On her Instagram right now, Miss Major has a recent photo of her newborn baby turned up toward her and sleeping. They're stunning together. The caption is "Muthahood." Her child is turned up to her like she's become the sky.

I recently googled "mother earth and father sky" for this book because I kept thinking about those terms in relationship to weather and how everyone seems to say them all the time but what do they even mean. I found myself on a subreddit about it and there was some agreement that it's "because the sky seeds the earth and the earth grows things."

But my favorite response on the thread was, "nah, it's because dads are distant like sky."

My girlfriend changed my name to Daddy in their phone today and I honestly don't know what to tell you, except I'm on an adventure.

Once, I opened Jo's apartment door and ran my hand along the wall to flip on the light. My outstretched arm was grabbed, then pinned behind my back, a fabric hood was pulled over my head.

She had two metal hooks between her fingers, she tugged one of the hooks across my chest.

I'm dragging you up Olympus to fuck, she said, settling onto my stomach. She yanked the hood off. The curtains that opened out onto the fire escape blew against her back. She'd covered herself in feathers. The curtain blew.

She was supposed to be Zeus. At the time I was thinking, not everyone gets to have a dad, and so I took my chance.

Do you know the story of Zeus and Ganymede? I just read Jericho Brown's poem about it:

"I mean don't you want God / To want you?"

I've wanted to tell you about those first ever sexual experiences in tornado chat rooms. I'd started one of my own. I made a logo where the *V* for vortex had a tornado in it. I'd read all the books about tornadoes I could find and we compared notes in those chat rooms. We talked about how chasing worked and where everyone was going.

I'd meet random guys in the chat rooms. It was quick:

somebody in a Jeep would pull up in the yard and we'd leave for the cigarette kiosk in the Kroger parking lot before heading out of town. There was generally the idea of a tornado. We'd have hail and good storms. We'd go north and out of state.

There was nothing like that feeling. The sky rips up light and pulls it in. Everyone has to get quiet. The body becomes sort of neon. Everyone gets so small. There's no shadows or anything. No one is in charge of anything, the sky is.

At the time, the coolest thing to do was to wear a WWJD bracelet and a Be Like Christ T-shirt and go to K-Life, where there'd be some dude with a guitar singing for a group of kids around bowls of Chex. I didn't participate in this. I once went to an after-school meeting for the Fellowship of Christian Athletes to get free bagels and my classmates were like why are you here?

If you don't know this, a big part of being in Dallas is church and there're activities for every night. You could shop around too. The Methodist church had this thing called WOW—Walk On Water—every Wednesday. It was in a church theatre with like fifty kids, dry ice, black lights, and lasers. If you guessed the bible verse right, you'd win some flip-flops or a Christian rock CD (which was also called WOW). I remember ironic SPAM-branded flip-flops being doled out the night I went. The Episcopal church wasn't jazzy like this, it was more like where the bad church kids went. The Presbyterians called them the Whiskey-palians.

My mom and I were going to the Potter's House. The Potter's House is one of the tenth biggest churches in the world. It's in Fort Worth so she'd take us to Krispy Kreme on the way. The jumbotron was the best. I'd get home and then go back on AOL. I didn't think much of using that massive PC to hang out in tornado chat rooms and meet dudes and talk about sex and eventually go with them wherever they were going.

This one guy had a big neon fish tank with white fish, in Plano or Richardson or something like that, and thick tan carpet, his parents were never home. He had a wet, red face and a pig kind of nose. I'd let him touch me with *Twister* on loop or the radar on.

Every window looked out onto a highway.

I didn't think about how it was all men in all the chat rooms and on all the chases. I did think to some extent that it was intense for me to go, which was evidenced by me telling no one in my family at all ever to this day.

Those years, like between the ages of eleven and thirteen, were really the time where I'd been trying to connect with my family but couldn't. What did I want in the weather? There's nothing I'd longed for more than to curl into a pile with them. Like with all of them. I wanted to be together and learn about them, whatever they liked and cared about, to breathe their breathing.

It didn't go like that though. I tried it everywhere else. For a long time, my everywhere else had been Jo.

• • •

Even at the very beginning of the tour, Derek regularly referenced *Moby Dick*. This is our white whale, he'd say, like here we go looking for it. He'd call himself captain sometimes.

I watched Derek do this toggling: he wanted to show us this ultimate giving in to a "natural force," a force greater than the state, capital, yet he was also trying to capture the thing, to get it on camera and win.

We really surrender to these storms, Derek would say. We just get on our knees and suck dick, he'd already said this a few times since I'd been in the van. People were used to it, so nobody said anything, just kept smiling. I'd be listening and sitting and sitting and feeling exactly like a child.

Just as I was considering all this, we had to stop because there was a bee in the car. June and Jamal both said stop stop with one voice. The bee was a dot moving through the shade of the van, its sound was louder than its body. Tony pulled over silently and without protest. We lumped onto the side of a gray road. Derek got out and opened both van doors. We filed out and everyone stood in the brush along the road. We waited for the bee.

Moz was someone who I wanted to become my friend, he was always joking, making jokes about being Punjabi, being a husky short king. I'm like that too. He'd become a storm legend in his town apparently.

I also wanted Jamal to become my friend. He spoke Arabic and a few other languages. He made a lot of jokes about the concept of BMIs coming from dead white men, and him and Derek being happy to be fat, obese by UK and American standards, they'd joke. The van was full of their laughing. This was his first time chasing, he said that it was a bucket list thing like gambling.

Everyone was eating candy and jerky and those freeze-dried knots of cheese from Starbucks. It was becoming clear that food was about gas stations and sometimes Walmart, which was actually the best somehow because of the variety.

We were north of Boulder now, had driven from Oklahoma City. I'd never been that north before, the plateaus were showing up. Everyone was giggling.

We'd gone to another Wendy's. The grass around it smelled like heaven and exhaust. It was a busy Wendy's actually. The heat was coming off the seat belts when we pulled in, and I thought how much hotter they'd be when we got back in the car. Any of you who grew up in a hot climate would hear me on this, those seat belts used to burn.

Inside, we stood in the blast of air-conditioning in a little clump, and Derek and Tony went to the bathroom. I hung back with Moz. We stood shoulder to shoulder for a few minutes without saying anything. My phone vibrated in the front pocket of my overalls. I pulled it out and it was Derek.

"Yr 'one of the boys' vibe is strong," it said.

I did not tell this to Moz. I didn't reply. What I wanted to say was that I'd been bleeding a lot lately. Like a little bit every day. I didn't particularly care, but my mood was also somewhat sour. A friend who'd been dealing with something similar said that my progesterone was probably low. I take birth control to regulate mine, she'd said. It is what it is.

What'd Derek mean by one of the boys vibes?

In the van I'd just watched a TikTok that went "You Don't Think Trans People Exist? You're Just Colonized" and had been reading Hil Malatino's book *Trans Care*.

"My own body was never—at the biological level and indeed, at the genital—neatly 'male' or 'female,'" Malatino writes. "The [colonizing] effort to rhetorically recode biology as binary is a direct denial of the biological diversity and exuberance of bodies, and the biologists already know this."

Malatino talks about how trans studies has encouraged the recognition of "the stitched-together, interactive constitution of all embodiment."

As one of my last social outings before leaving LA, I got to go to Isabella Rossellini's show *Link Link Circus*.

I was excited because my grandmother was a big fan of her mother's and I was happy to be near her. I'd also loved Rossellini's *Green Porno*, a series of short films produced for Sundance in which Rossellini gives a chronology of genitals: ducks can switch their vaginal canals around if they don't want a certain mate, barnacles can just literally become sperm and impregnate themselves, it's actually endless, the combinations of reproductive techniques and the looseness of their connection to sexuality and gender—this is her point. White supremacy and colonization have imposed a kind of morality on sexuality and gender and use the idea of "natural" as a way to reinforce it. But we're so wrong about nature, she's saying.

In this book's original draft, before I had started T, I wrote:

Sometimes I wake up to this fantasy of control. Like maybe I could rule over my body, if nothing else. I could tell it what to do and control how it looks and behaves. But this couldn't be further from real. It slips away from me regardless.

I always thought that, you know, even though it's ridiculous, deep down maybe going on hormones would be an attempt to control my body and how I'm seen, but it's way more fun than that, I realize now. It's a ride. Really, the control was in my denial of this desire, like white-knuckling. Eventually, I'd started thinking, what could be more natural than want?

. . .

The only other tornado I've seen, besides the one that hit while Gunner was watching *Bambi*, happened in that same town—Glen Rose.

There was one attendant in the restaurant and a TV hung from the ceiling, pointed at the three picnic tables outside. A red scroll was squealing across the TV, a weather map broke through the broadcast with a radar picture. Bow Echo. Glen Rose.

We shrugged, watched the sky go green, a stack of napkins lifted off the table, not blowing. Hank came back with a greasy bag and we pointed at the TV.

Fat droplets of rain lost themselves across the cars in the parking lot. Shit, he'd said.

Had we seen it or just heard it? It was there. The breath of it made ours quicker, it was an incredible rapture—the closest I'd been. The clouds came all the way down to sort of kiss us. My hair went toward it, every hair on my body. The light was starry and green. We'd stopped, all four of us. Tye even stopped bouncing the basketball we'd just gotten at Walmart or somewhere. Nobody moved except the leaves on the trees, which made themselves into cups for the downpour. We looked into the sky and when it turned purple Hank yelled for us to get in the car and he never is serious about danger so we did as he said. We didn't particularly hurry though.

Mom was back at the campsite where we'd left her. This was our last family trip ever. I don't think I've seen all four of them in the same place since. It ended like this. Wet lights were moving on the road up the hill. As we pulled into the parking lot of the campground, we saw a line of ambulances, one cop car. Everything else was green.

Marie, Hank said with his hands still on the steering wheel because he knew it was for Mom.

The storm had gone white-gray behind us. It had let go of all of its rain.

Hank became responsible for Mom again then. She was wrapped in a green blanket, standing in the rain with all these EMTs. She'd almost died from an overdose. Had left all her clothes somewhere.

The body of somebody else, anybody else, is always a call.

My grandma always says that someone's quality of life is dependent on the choices that they make, which isn't ever exactly true, but I grew up with that hypervigilance about making the "right" ones. I always try to be responsible, to respond correctly. Still, if my self is also like a ringing phone, I've been ignoring all of that.

Hank had decided to answer my mom's call again. He and my brothers were going to move in with Mom and I couldn't go.

The guy that had been my best protector and advocate for the better part of two years—the one place I'd been invited to live and try to feel safe—had succumbed to something. Was it love? He'd been defeated. We fell.

At the Wendy's I put my phone back in my overall bib pocket or whatever that's called and I shifted on my feet next to Moz. None of the tourists looked at their phone as much as I did. They wanted to look around.

Those new automated kiosks were glowing at us.

Why did you get into this? he turned to ask me and I said, I'm getting divorced, before I actually had decided to get divorced.

Why did you? I nodded back.

The energy going to the LED posters near us was loud.

My brother, he said.

Oh yeah?

I leaned forward to hear. I always like sibling stuff.

Yeah, he loved weather like this, he was really into it. He got me into it, Moz said, raising his eyes to mine. He killed himself. It was seven years ago.

Moz leaned when he said it, like he might lean into me, and I put my arm out. But he was actually wiping his nose in a quiet way.

We stood there together with the Wendy's ads, the other chasers, and didn't really move.

Well, he said, I'm glad we're here. And picked up his shake.

When we got back into the van, everyone kept saying things like on their 2016 tour, for example, they'd had nearly twenty tornadoes by now.

Someone with a dramatic, colorful parrot on his shoulder walked in front of the van.

Tony was like, don't we know it. But there was a delay because we'd all looked at the parrot/pirate guy for a minute. We'd driven all day. No weather happened, but we'd almost made it to Minnesota—that was something.

DADDY BOY

Derek smelled really good and if you asked anyone, they'd tell you he's why they were there. He lived in Storm Travelers merchandise. He was fun. Everything about him was fun. He held his body out in a protective, knowing way. He'd look in the rearview mirror at us all and check. He'd knock on our knees as a joke. He'd be cheery and then serious and everyone felt like they'd returned to something, some kind of core connectedness that depended upon a shepherd, someone who knew more, and relaxed into that.

By the time we pulled into Deadwood, or the hotel there, our surroundings had gone from flat plains to three- and four-story density—a brick downtown with thin streets.

THE REAL SIN CITY said a red yard sign stuck into a small park as we drove in. There was a mural of a red-eyed, pink-skinned angry person panning for gold. When we pulled up to the hotel, Derek was swirling a Big Gulp and explaining Wounded Knee to the British, playing the Indigo Girls as explanation—their cover of Buffy Sainte-Marie's "Bury My Heart at Wounded Knee." Everyone in the car leaned forward and listened.

If you search videos of Deadwood, there're several iPhone ones of gun fight reenactments in the street blocked off by traffic cones. They're shooting blanks and crowds gather and film.

Everywhere you go, it's like a car commercial, chirps a tour guide in one video, showing off Mount Rushmore.

"A tourist mecca cut from stone and a sinister delusion of destiny," Ron Way writes in the *Star Tribune* of Mount Rushmore. It's widely known that the creator of Mount Rushmore was a member of the KKK, which was a big funder of the monument, intended to be a sculpture of the fathers of the confederacy. Not only is this sculpture deeply anti-Black, but, of course, it was erected on stolen land, which the US acknowledged via the 1980 Supreme Court agreement that ordered the federal government to compensate eight tribes for the seized land.

"Lakota see the faces of men who lied, cheated and murdered innocent people whose only crime was living on land they wanted to steal," said Harold Frazier, chairman of the Cheyenne River Sioux, who called for the removal of the monument in 2020, as reported on by the *Washington Post*.

We can't have a good road trip without some Indigo Girls, Tony'd said and I shook my head like maybe I was hearing him wrong. He wasn't joking. I hadn't met any straight dude ever who'd said something like that.

The night before, our first night, I heard someone talking so sweet through the wall—

Yeah baby, I heard, I love you baby. Can we do that when I get home?

Then when it got quiet I heard Childish Gambino's "This is America" pumping—that summer it was pumping.

The listener kept turning it up for the end: "You just a barcode, yeah."

While we waited in a line of cars inching up to the hotel in Deadwood that second day, Derek pulled the music video up on his computer and I realized it was him in the other room talking so sweet. He'd turned it up at the end for everyone in the van.

We pulled into the parking lot and Derek got out of the car laughing because Moz had said something funny.

Tony pulled out our suitcases from the back and Derek went in first like we'd gotten used to him doing, to organize the room keys.

Inside the lobby was gold, smoky mauve carpet with a mini golf thing indoors.

I looked around for food. The others left for their rooms while I was looking. Derek found me at the vending machines to give me my room card—

How's it going so far? he asked, leaning against the soda machine. It's intense, I said, because I was hungry.

Well, I hope you feel like you can be comfortable. I get it to some extent, my girlfriend is trans, so I know it can be...

I didn't hear the end because my Snickers shot through the vending machine so loud.

I didn't want to hear the end. I don't know why except I was uncomfortable and growing more so because the Midwest was Jo's world. I'd just started having thoughts about it. I'd only been twice and both times were with her. People often thought she was European because she'd shifted her Midwestern accent to lay down in such a way that she sounded far from there. I'd come to visit her parents. They were super close. She was an only child. They taught me how to make gnocchi. I'd finally been invited in after the wedding and I won at quarters. Her dad, a stoic guy with a handlebar mustache, cried when we got married. I looked at all that blonde wood through the window of the van. I wanted to text them.

Earlier that day, we'd stopped at a place with faux carvings of bears and moose and things in the vinyl siding. It was a proper restaurant, our first real one on the tour. The menu was plastic-looking with white wood, all over the room people were smiling with their eyes only, mouths in one long line.

We were close to the airport Jo's parents picked us up from toward the end of our relationship. It was my last time seeing them. They'd picked us up in their four-door truck after a late flight. I was so tired and not feeling well. I don't remember much of what was going on.

Jo's mom spoke to me and we really liked each other, so I thought I'd said, yes, absolutely or something cheery but I felt something on my knee and it was Jo's hand pinching it and my mom had done the exact same thing to me when I was little when we rode around with my grandparents.

Don't talk to them like that, she was saying and I had no idea what I'd done to warrant it.

I'd loved these corrections at first because I literally felt like I knew nothing. Jo's dominance gave me a structure and I guess that's what support is or whatever.

But that day my whole self dropped from my stomach to my feet, to my face, which reddened.

In the restaurant, I heard Jo's parents' accents and kept my head down. Derek was talking to someone who asked why there were no tornado magnets on the side of the van yet— Storm Travelers had these hand-sized magnets that they kept in the glove compartment to mark when a tornado was spotted. They would go on the side of the van like a football helmet—we had none. It was already fairly late in the season. Derek and Tony were watching the radar scroll on a TV and palming their faces, it's getting worse somehow, Derek said. One of the people serving us was like you better take those storms somewhere else. We were like, there aren't any.

On the way to our hotel that night, the van was silent all around. We 'd made up a mission, but it was only made up.

What does it mean to try? It was late, the person next to me was the one I knew the least, Samuel. He looked like an EDM fan, was the most muscled, the most quiet. He had a lot of red underneath his eyes, he'd joined to take photos, they all did. His hands were on his thighs.

I didn't stand out against this group as much as I thought I would. We may not see a tornado or even a thunderstorm, I figured. This was a new realization.

The shadow of the pen in my hand was enormous across the van walls, its canvas ceiling. There were empty water bottles and cups rolling around, sour mouth smells. Tony in front of me was massaging his ear in the dark. It was soft to watch. His ear turned red, thick and happy.

Tye texted me to say my dog was fine but was pooping nonstop. I guess she's nervous, he said, but texted me a picture of her tangled in his sheets—she was sleeping with him every night, her body about the size of his forearm.

I used to visit my paternal grandmother when I was living with my maternal grandparents as a kid, and then also when I lived in New York. I'd take the train to her house and was excited to be involved. She had this picture frame in her kitchen that had been there for decades—it's the kind with the circle windows, you know what I mean? Pictures of family groupings.

My dad and his wife have a circle, their daughters do, each of my cousins, all their parents.

These dogs have one too. There are these two black and white dogs in their own circle and I was the only person out of three generations without one.

I think about those circles on the family photo wall thing and I guess it makes sense to want one and to want one enough that I ignore what I already have. Am I Hank's?

Hank has a lot of photos of me actually. It's clear they are from different times and locations than the ones with the boys in them. I'm always in my own frame with a unique background (the boys are together or sharing a background in each photo), but I'm there. He's got one with me in an orange and red striped shirt with no teeth. I'm also roller-skating with one leg up going down our street in Sacramento. In another, he's standing with me and I have a fanny pack shaped like a duck with my tape player in it.

I was reflecting on this and looking at Tye 's texts from my spot behind Tony.

I'd spent so much of my life wondering how to get a circle on that woman's wall.

Come to Papa, Derek was saying to the radar.

There was hope today. It was small, we'd woken up in Deadwood and would drive back down south, this would be our only time so far north and I'd realized that maybe we'd gone far up just because it was something to do.

Was it Kansas where we're going now?

Derek pointed out some of the cells on the radar as we drove. The days were going like this: we'd get up and leave our hotel rooms at 8 a.m.

They were always the same, as motels are, and you know to tip a ton, right? Like as much as you can.

We only stayed in the chain ones, so it was soft and predictable like that.

I'd pull all the sheets off in the morning and order the piles between big and small towels because this is what my mom did for a job so I'd do what she says she likes.

I'd use the K-Cup in the room and then stretch. There wasn't much time for anything else. I'd get a banana from downstairs or an apple.

DADDY BOY

Does everyone else's childhood wash them like this?

Mine washes all night.

I'd eat my banana during our meeting and every day we'd pile our stuff in the lobby and sit around a decorative gas or LED fireplace or whatever the hotel had. All the patterns of low pile fabric against the backdrop of the popcorn ceiling and walls. We'd sit there with sunscreen and mouthwash smells while Derek would be like, here goes.

I wondered if everyone else also pictured him and Tony wearing their boxers and sipping from old sodas planning this?

I guess he was aiming to use a combination of intuition and science. Like the models were supposed to be our guide: the radar maps published daily by global atmospheric monitoring systems that show the low pressure and jet streams and where lines of storms could form and at what time. There are several models and sometimes they say the storms will be this far east and then everybody goes over there, but there'd also be a chance of something happening to the north and the people who take that track end up alone and victorious (meaning they find a tornado and get it on camera). They succeed. The trick though is that often there aren't any storm clouds to read in the morning, you have to wait because these storms are created by some combination of convection, dew point, and humidity and you can't know until you know.

Derek would explain that the low would move, maybe, across the plains that day. No one questioned him. They put new camera batteries in and snacked.

I felt focused. I'd watch a fly land on Derek's thumb, for example, while he scrolled through the forecasts for the day. He'd shake his thumb and it would return and that's all. We'd made it to the Nebraska–Kansas line. We were headed to Walmart. I liked getting those pickles in a plastic bag, but by the time I'd finished the self-checkout with the pickles, everyone was shuffling around outside the van. It's starting to rain, Derek said. Plastic rustled. Clouds were coming up from the northwest and raking toward the ground in the parking lot.

On a tornado chasing tour, rain is kryptonite because the rain wets the sky and blocks any possible photo. It wasn't a hard rain that was starting up, just misty.

Well how about we just get set up for tomorrow then, Derek said, looking at Tony.

Yeah man, get us out of here, Jamal joked.

I will, I will, Derek said, clicking around on his laptop.

Derek was particularly concerned about Jamal and his experience of the trip. Jamal was the only one of us who'd never been chasing before.

You good, man? he'd asked as we were getting into the van this morning, wrapping his arm around Jamal to be close and to check.

I'm real good, he'd said and they walked together sharing some of that freeze-dried cheese.

The new plan was to revisit the models and see if we could put ourselves in good position for the next day.

You know what, Derek said as we 'd pulled away from the Walmart, let's just go down here, he 'd pointed to a dirt road on our left.

Here?

Yeah, let's just go down there. Derek clicked around some more on his laptop and looked at the sky and was like, yeah, this works. As Tony slowed the van, Derek messed with him, put his hand in Tony's armpit and left it there, like hello.

They flirted.

A small cloud had mushroomed off to our left with a flat base and scud crushing out. It was little but it was there. We tugged the van along this dirt road to a ridge. It was afternoon now with flashes of lightning far off.

Derek had us pull onto the ridge facing out.

Why don't you guys see what you can get? He wiped his face with both of his hands when he said it. The tourists shuffled out with camera equipment, all the things. They looked off at a hazy patch of cloud. They seemed fine, their shoulders brushing. The van door was closed to them. Tony, Derek, and I were alone.

We may have a trough on Sunday, but that's it, Derek said looking at Tony. It felt like they forgot I was there.

The trough is dying. Any other year, it'd be popping, Tony said.

This is the part where I lose my mind, said Derek. He put his forefinger and thumb on the bridge of his nose and breathed.

Friday is bullshit, Saturday is really weak, Sunday the low is bad, there's not even upslope plays, he said, opening his eyes again for Tony.

Nothing you can do, man, it's an ugly year. Tony pressed on the down window button just to hear the sound maybe. David Copperfield us a tornado, man, he'd said. Trucks rattled past.

I used to be able to pull storms out of my ass, Derek was saying, I can't do it this year and it's fucking with me.

Feels like the mechanics of the earth are dying, Tony said, putting both his hands on the steering wheel and moving it back and forth, inert.

The tourists were talking but we couldn't hear. They were taking quiet photos from the ridge, of a train against the blue/black background. The contrast of the train was bright: red stoplight, blue background. There was a farmhouse behind us, a mockingbird too. These clouds promised so much, they had what looked like bellies full of rain but there was nothing in them actually. Or if there was, it wasn't enough. There were coal piles on the midline. All the red got white in the light. The grass popped. Nothing made lightning, we sure didn't.

When they got back in the van, Derek was picking at his beard and answering questions. I got quiet in the car wishing for candy or dinner.

The light rain was stinking on all our bodies. We stopped at another gas station, they had no postcards.

When we got to the Days Inn, Samuel and June were talking softly about something and the train trestles were singing. I wondered if they might have sex.

Tony got out to do the job of shuffling our bags around and handing them to us. I stood next to him in the heat. He'd started talking to me about rites of passage. He talked about how he's still a kid and has trouble with work and relationships because of it. He realizes he's entitled as a white guy and thinks that other people will do things for him. Tony's dependence on Derek looks consensual, so that is nice, but Tony was describing a desire for independence. Like I should learn to do some things on my own. What about interdependence? I said. I've learned so much about interdependence as part of disabled communities I belong to, the idea of independence as a goal is ridiculous because we're all just temporarily abled, right? We need each other.

In 2014, I got to go see that play *Straight White Men* by Young Jean Lee. I went with my friend Nancy to the theatre in Culver City and I hadn't been to a play in forever, but I'd really wanted to see this one. Have you heard of it?

Lee did an interview with *GQ* where she explains that the play's inception was a workshop "with a bunch [of] women, queer people, people of color, and I asked them, 'What do you think of straight white men?' And they said all of these really terrible things and then I said, 'Well okay, what would you rather that they be like?' They gave me a list of things that they wanted straight white men to do and be, so I wrote those down and I went and I wrote the character of Matt. I brought him back in, I thought they were just gonna love him, and they all hated him."

I was really struck by Matt in the play, who'd been written to fill the space left by his mother, who'd recently passed, as a caregiver for the father. All seems okay for them both, they like the arrangement of Matt cleaning and cooking, but when Matt's two brothers come home for the holidays, they convince the dad that he 's being too lax and letting Matt just fail by not doing anything with his life— because housework and caregiving as a career is unacceptable for dudes in this subject position—the dad kicks Matt out.

"I mean, audiences respond to the character of Matt very similarly to how his family responds, they're really bugged by him on a deep level because he's very antithetical to some of our values as Americans living in a capitalist society," Lee says in GQ, he's not "independent" because he's not a successful capitalist.

Tony was clearly wrestling with this as he noticed everyone else having marginalized identity conversations and bonding over it. What if we talked about being broke? he'd said and laughed. Then he asked me if I believed in the principle of writing what you know versus what you don't and at the same time he brushed off a daddy longlegs that had slipped onto his neck.

We just had a conversation at the college I work for about IRB, the process where we review research that students are doing to make sure it's ethical, for example, and sound. The conversation moved to whether or not we could successfully apply this practice of IRB to art. Should we be including "the arts" in this idea of research ethics? My work was brought up: am I thinking of the characters in my nonfiction as "subjects"? Was I out here on this tour trying to interface with this subject position, the white man, in a sort of safe way? Was

I studying this guy? I don't really need to study whiteness or man-ness—most of us are versed in these subjects as people in the world—and at the same time, like Lee, I wonder if I'd wanted to tease apart these categories a little. I do want to understand my family in order to be close. Yet, the more I try, the further I feel.

In bed at the motel that night, I really contemplated giving up. I tried to bring the feeling into my body. I had pushed the rough floral duvet off the bed and cracked the window as far as it would open so there might be a breeze, about an inch or two. I listened to the hum of the mini fridge and the ambient noise of vents turning on and off in other rooms. I breathed. Maybe giving up is the same as letting my body just breathe, there in that weird room. I tried to relax. I pictured blocking Tye and Gunner on my phone, blocking everybody, throwing my phone out the window, walking into the brush outside, going to sleep under some tree. It did feel sort of nice to imagine.

• • •

The next morning, Jamal and Tony were talking about how the landscape looked exactly like the Windows 95 background. We were hurling south from our hotel. Billboards ripped by. There was a person nearly in the median under a silver Corolla, legs curled up like a deer.

It's not looking that good, Derek was saying as part of his

morning talk, but we'll have fun for sure. He'd been saying this a lot. The computer and jokes on the computer were growing important. Someone had eaten a mint that smelled up the whole car.

There were antelope on the left to look at instead of storms, the sun washed the front of the car. The cows were littered. A number of people in the van began chewing. This was a game about waiting. This was also a game about powerlessness, an expensive game. It was a different kind of powerlessness than everyone came looking for—this powerlessness of not being able to conjure a storm doesn't seem as good as the powerlessness of being subject to a storm. But honestly, I was fascinated that true surrender to nature can also look like the absolute lack of a show, a storm—that this is really it. The internet went down. There was a layer of mashed bug across the windows. I found myself closing my eyes to leave.

All the storms look like shit, Derek was saying to everyone and everyone already knew. He had put his hat back on after he took it off. He was mostly cracking jokes, but had his arms near to his body and was watching the cell dissipate on the radar and breathing soft out of his nose. All the chasers were scattered ants.

The models looked bad last night but they looked better than they do now, Derek was saying into the far back of the van. He also said fuck fuck fuck softly to himself because there were so few storms, the pressure not to miss one was big.

There was a tractor plowing one field over, probably the farmer was grateful for the sun. Someone was snoring. A train full of coal moved left. Convection is beautiful. The van got stuck behind another Corolla. Everyone was breathing out. The pressure was a kind of glue. We'd passed a sign that said kid fireworks with a cartoon black cat made out of shingles on it. I touched the slight seat belt rash on my neck. It was only day three.

Sometimes though, when no storms emerged, the clouds were perfect like a big flower, dust becoming water.

We 'd dropped Derek off at a Holiday Inn Express. I found out later that this is where he likes to poop. We never stayed at any Holiday Inn Express, they were too fancy for us, we just stopped there for this reason. I guess their lobby bathrooms have nice soap. There was a convergence of storm chasers in the area again. The other vans were zipping south. There was a tornado that we'd missed in New Mexico, everyone else was in New Mexico and no one knows why we had gone so far north on the first day and missed it.

Derek got back in the van and scrolled with his wireless mouse, looked at the base of a weak storm through the windshield that we'd driven an hour to get to. He started laughing. Fuck, he was saying, Jesus Christ. There's not even reason to get out of the car at this point. We pulled into a farmhouse driveway.

DADDY BOY

Every storm we drive to dies, he was saying. But, the pink was coming out. Pink with dirt.

Okay, boys and girls and people, he said, pulling out a Stallion candy cigarette and putting it between his lips. We're aiming toward the Brazos! There were low shrubs everywhere, little spread brush, dead trees. The trees here always look so spent.

Our midday stop was a Dollar General and I sat in the van waiting, overheating. The Brits were on fire. There was a Chevy next to us that'd been eaten up by rust. We were not far from Dallas but not near enough.

We'd made it to the tree-lined, river-running plains. It was our first time in this topography all tour. I'd been waiting for it.

This is just like Jarrell, Derek kept saying, he was saying it quietly and sitting forward. The cape is the same. He was feeling hyped, bouncing a little in his seat and holding onto the handle above the passenger side window.

Goddamn, I like it when a plan comes together, Derek was saying, smoking on his candy.

No one asked what the cape was and I'm not sure if it's because everyone knew but me or if all of us were pretending. I wondered if the cape was even good. Like is this a performance? Like WWF? How is this all that different than the Twister ride at Universal Studios my grandparents took me to? It was the only ride I'd wanted to go on and they were disappointed that we'd gone all the way to Universal Studios and I didn't care. The ride was boring. You walked onto a platform that shifted side to side and up and down when a CGI tornado came on a large screen at the back of the theatre and "wiped out" the gas station in front of you. It makes me think of those inflatable children's slides that are shaped like a sinking *Titanic*.

We stopped at another Holiday Inn Express.

All the tourists were completely fine to wait for Derek in the parking lot because it was good for all of us when he went to poop: it meant he was excited.

But by the time he got back into the van, the cell we'd been focused on was weakening on the radar. The markers that had been bright red were becoming more and more orange, then yellow, and then it was just green.

Moz leaned over to be like, it's going to be nothing, but we'll pretend we're excited for him.

In the parking lot, June confronted Derek. We could hear it from in the van. I guess she'd been talking to some of her other chaser friends at our last gas station stop. We'd all seen her with her hands on her hips. I guess they'd told her they were going somewhere else and we were stupid for following this moisture trough because it was going to do nothing.

DADDY BOY

We watched Derek try to defend his choices and then you could see him sort of give up into joking around. He pretended to reach for his shirt in the back and pull it off over his head like it was hockey, he mimed throwing gloves off and onto the ground. June smiled and pantomimed shoving him.

When he got back in the van, he moved his mouse around on the dash with the candy cigarette hanging out of his mouth. A dot of red had shown up in the green.

It's a very good thing, you fuckers, he said. Look at that.

The cows were busy in the field below us.

Driving is the hardest part of all of this, no roads, you know? And dirt ones become wet and impassible during a downpour. We weren't ever fast enough.

They severe-warned it, Derek said as we drove toward the cloud base, he'd been smoking the candy for emphasis.

The tourists pressed against the windows with their shoes on their hands to make the glare go away. They found a lion's head in the cloud and everyone leaned out the window with cameras.

It was Moz's birthday, I'd just found out, and every time he leaned forward, there was crinkling from cookies he'd gotten as a present from the hotel that morning.

We drove parallel to Amarillo to get at this storm base. It smelled like campfire out the window for no reason when someone said, Amarillo eighty-three miles. I wouldn't have known without the signage that we were anywhere nearby, but then there was that same pink of the Palo Duro Canyon and I remembered when I ran out of gas with my friend Jenny out here once on our way from Dallas to Denver and we stopped at Hank's parents for bologna sandwiches while we waited for a tow. That was my only other time being in Amarillo without Hank. I am so unlike him, I was thinking, watching all that pink show up. I'm unlike him in the way that he feels comfortable with the yellow/brown. I didn't want to be there any longer than I was supposed to be. It felt good in an intellectual way to see Amarillo on the sign, but the yellow/brown always made me want to run. The green/black/blue of the East Coast has more of the sensation in my eyes that I like. I felt around for the difference in my stomach. Derek was car dancing to nothing, looking at the radar for rotation, again, again.

It's a lone supercell hanging on the edge of an outflow boundary, he said. This has a chance.

He rolled his window down to check the airflow, and all of a sudden I remembered that I'd had a dream the night before about a really mild tornado. In the dream I bothered my dad about it, the dad that isn't Hank, and made him come over. As he was arriving to the scene where there was a dream tornado on the ground, it died. I woke up.

It's gonna happen, Derek said. A few bright hail balls were chucked from the cloud, from the most purple part. They looked amazing against the purple. The feeling was bright, basically.

The van was pulled over and Derek had thrown the passenger side door open. He was hanging on it.

The van was silent some more.

He crossed his arms and tossed his mouse on the dash, authoritative. The sun broke through and made things windy.

The best is this purple and its tremendous contrast. Mounting purple. Everyone was silent in the van except for Derek's near- whispered instructions for Tony, trying to get us into a spot we could escape from if we have to. That really is the biggest problem. The van is heavy and it would be easy to end up on a dirt road in a downpour. I guess that's how the guys in Twistex died. The El Reno tornado changed direction on them and they were stuck.

We parked in the panhandle within sight of one farmhouse and one tarred road not too far off. It was level and dirt and surrounded by a field of ankle-high grass. We got out to feel it. The point is for the forecaster and the driver to put the van in a good spot for pictures, which meant not being exactly in the line of the storm, but actually just to the side, so you can watch it, but not be in the rain.

This aggravated me. I've always loved the approach, not knowing if there will be hail that's dangerous or lightning that catches fire. It's perfect to watch it come, to take precautions—like to unplug computers and stand away from the windows or whatever—and then to let go and wait.

When we got out, it was hard to close the van doors because of the wind. Birds were flying into the storm in ways that made their bodies so lit up. Hail was falling onto us and another car idling near by, they'd followed us to get to the storm, which made so much sense to me, it was something I'd do too. Now they were in their car alongside us and waiting.

Didn't I tell you? Derek was saying. This is Jarrell 2.0. And no one believed me about Jarrell, either, everybody was like, not a chance, but look what happened!

The Jarrell tornado, apparently, was in this same part of Texas around this same time of year, and didn't look right on radar. Jarrell produced granulated debris, Derek went on, meaning everything in the tornado's path had become just particles. Derek had caught the storm perfectly and took some viral photos and videos. Part of this game is being where the other chasers are not. When all the chasers go to the same place, it's called convergence and it sucks for a number of reasons: easier to get stuck in traffic, which is dangerous; competition for good positioning, which can also be dangerous; and basically taking the same photos as everyone else, which is deemed sort of pathetic.

Derek wandered around the van, which he doesn't always do. Look at that horseshoe, he said, sweaty and proud. Did he give birth? There was a rainbow, too, the flat base was making figures of light pop out of the dark and it was spinning slightly.

I could see a woman standing on the porch of her farmhouse nearby. She spotted our van. She came out with someone else in a straw hat and a flannel.

Is it going to hit us? she hollered over. Are we going to be okay?

Watch the sky, be safe, Derek called back. We all walked toward the farmhouse. The skin around Derek's eyes reddened and he put his hand up to shield his face.

June turned toward the woman like she might talk, but she was just taking a selfie next to the farmhouse fence with the supercell behind her. The couple didn't seem to notice. Her phone made its loud imitation shutter sound.

The cloud above their house was the one we were watching. Could drop a funnel anytime it seems, the lady said, but it did look a lot worse earlier, she nodded and then walked back up her drive.

It was a surprise to hear her say it was looking weaker because of how lit up everything felt. But I did have the sort of sense that it wasn't ramping up, the wind had slowed a bit, and the light was starting to pour in from the east.

Derek turned away from her toward the scud that was rising. This motherfucker is going to try, he said. He was shaking the last candy cigarette out of its box. I wanted one.

The best modules didn't show this, he'd said. I see the result of the models. It's a southwest moving storm.

We stood there watching the scud for a while as the sun pushed back out. The virga didn't do the thing it was supposed to do. A lot of people think they see a funnel when it's really RFD, which comes out the back of the wall cloud like the foot of a clam, or a penis. But that's not the funnel. The funnel forms when scud gets sucked up by a rotating wall cloud—it gets sucked up and then pushed back to the ground in this weird and magical way.

None of that was happening. Instead the scud was drifting off in different directions and graying because the rain was making it through. No funnel comes out of that. Derek was still not totally defeated when we got back in the van.

Seriously though, he'd said, if those two storms had linked up, Kilgore would have been wiped off the map.

Everyone is happier than I am, was my thought as we pulled out.

The flags in town were wagging. The Conoco was lit up purple/green just like in movies, we were in Shamrock, Texas, it was suddenly deep night.

I'm thinking of a number between one and one thousand, Derek said—we were so quickly back to this. We were tired. This was the first time I felt like this tour was sucking. I'd borrowed Samuel's red flashlight. I don't know what the red setting is for, but Tony and Derek said they were bothered by me writing by my regular flashlight in the van at night, so we'd decided I could use the red setting because it was less of an affront.

Jerrell had zero percent survival, Tony said out of nowhere into the dark.

The woman at the farmhouse today was sucking on her teeth and smiling, smelling like cookies. The guy she was with and the other person parked nearby were older, pulling down ball caps, farmers maybe, settler-descended probably.

We watched the storm die. The cloud we'd liked had become a sad flap—it's not going to look traditional, Derek had said as it ate itself. All the TVs in Shamrock had softball on.

In the dark, we pulled around the towns that all could have been Hico with their prominent gas stations and beautiful low buildings with short porches close to each other on a main cobblestone street. I started thinking about Hico and how maybe I like *The Collected Works of Billy the Kid* because it is all about these redacted photos. I thought of that photo Mom had taken of Tye, Gunner, Hank. How everyone was taking so many photos on this tour, how I wanted to take some myself, right now, especially since I'd made it where I wanted to go. I wanted to mark being near Amarillo, but it was all dark. In *The Collected Works of Billy the Kid*, Ondaatje draws a square on certain pages as if to contain a photo, but there's nothing in the square. He then captions the empty space. This is similar to Hervé Guibert's collection *Ghost Image*.

The reverse capture interests me.

Like this:

In 1880 a traveling photographer came through Fort Sumner. Billy posed standing in the street near old Beaver Smith's saloon. The picture makes him rough and uncouth.

The expression of his face was really boyish and pleasant. He may have worn such clothes as appear in the picture out on the range, but in Sumner he was careful of his personal appearance and dressed neatly and in good taste. I never liked the picture. I don't think it did Billy justice.

What does it mean to just let something go like rain down a window in that very specific way?

Like there's nowhere to go. There were two weeks more of this trip, some of the tourists would be on this tour for a month or more, I'd opted for the ten-day version.

What are we trying to get from taking these photos is something I wondered all the time. Is it the act of trying that's exciting, or is it the competition at this point: videos and likes and paid ads and that whole thing?

"One thing I have noticed is that some male chasers will attempt to belittle the experiences of others behind their backs," Shannon Key writes, about storm chasing being "male" dominated. "Remarks like, 'I mean, look at that, that's not a wedge, how can he call that a "wedge?"'"

She thinks of it in an essentialist sense: "One thing which I doubt we can change is that in general women are more interested in what goes on inside people, and men are more interested in what goes on outside people." Lol. I kept reading though because I did want to hear what Key said about the "male competitiveness" that dominates chasing. "Whose fault is it? Is it anyone's fault? Is it everyone's fault?" she asks.

I wonder sometimes if the "femininity" that people tease out around Billy the Kid has to do with the way his relationships are characterized—competitive, yes, I guess. But also, close.

Ondaatje:

Two years ago Charlie Bowdre and I criss-crossed the Canadian border... our horses stepped from country to country, across low rivers, through different colors of tree. The two of us, our criss-cross like a whip in slow motion, the ridge of action rising and falling, getting narrower in radius till it ended and we drifted down to Mexico and old heat. That there is nothing of depth, of significant accuracy, of wealth in the image, I know. It is there for a beginning.

Ontaanje makes their relationship so soft against all this violence.

"Blood a necklace on me all my life," Ondaatje writes in Billy's voice—throughout the book, Ondaatje animates Billy's autobiography with his own voice, like Gertrude Stein does in *The Autobiography of Alice B. Toklas.*

I'm reading that Jared Yates Sexton book right now about how (cisgender, white) men in the US have been culturally constructed and how violence is a very central part of that. Like, there's this function of "manhood" that says if you have any feeling at all, it's supposed to be anger, as opposed to shame or whatever. Sexton describes the time when a tree came down on his property in Georgia and all his neighbors made disapproving *huhs* when they realized he didn't have his own chainsaw. One even rode by in a tricked-out golf cart (author's description) and sort of ominously shook his head in disapproval as Sexton cleaned up the sawed bits of tree left behind after his neighbors eventually took care of the whole thing.

"The American man adapted his idea of self-worth to depend on his identity as a laborer," Sexton writes about (white) working men in the US. The issue, he lays out, is that they can't seem to earn wealth like they were told was their right. "In essence, American masculinity, or rather, the lie of American masculinity, became another product," Sexton writes, using the term "product" to emphasize the way this idea of masculinity was sold to the people, and functioned to generate a tireless source of labor in order, ultimately, to create profit for those in power. Fundamentally, the patriarchal system is "a fabricated state of being at odds with itself."

This is where violence comes in, according to Sexton. Rather than feeling shame, or really anything, they're taught to attack.

"Violence serves as an acceptable form of communication for men," Sexton writes, listing all the abuses he and his mom suffered at the hands of insecure dudes.

In *An Indigenous People's History of the United States*, Roxanne Dunbar-Ortiz cites "the continued popularity of, and respect for, the genocidal sociopath Andrew Jackson" as evidence that violence serves as the basis for the US masculine identity. "Men such as Robert Rogers, Daniel Boone, John Sevier, and David Crockett," she goes on to say, "as well as fictitious ones created by James Fenimore Cooper and other best-selling writers, call to mind D. H. Lawrence's 'myth of the essential white American'— that the 'essential American soul' is a killer."

This killer thing, the violence, seems to go hand-in-hand with expectations of mastery, and the aloneness that comes with that.

I had the same feeling as Sexton did with his chainsaw when, at twenty, I got that assistant building manager job in New York because I was flirting with people who wanted help putting AC units in their windows. I was hoping to learn how to do "handy" things from my boss and was wondering about my value and was struggling to find it. I thought maybe the only reason these people would want to date me is if I could do this kind of thing. I felt like I had to do it right and that if I fucked up, I'd be kicked out or something. This is such a lonely prospect. Who was I competing with? I hate to be wrong about anything.

I met Jo then. I wanted her to know me. She was wearing this black onesie and Toms and she looked summery and tan and I leaned onto the desk and was like, do you have any interest in talking about strap-ons with me? Like I want to know what I'm doing, I'd said. She was often talking about being a full-time domme and kink and toys.

The rest of the building was dark and nice. Only the hallway lights were on. I'd sleep in there sometimes when I was working late because often the train wouldn't go to where I lived in Brooklyn after 1 a.m. so I'd just move a bunch of massage blankets together and curl up in one of the offices. I was the one who opened in the mornings and I was also the one who was supposed to watch all security camera footage anyway.

There was something surprising about Jo's attention. She was looking directly at me, her onesie straps moved on and off her shoulders. I asked her about this person I was trying to date who'd called me a muffin after we'd had sex. I was into having threesomes with her and her boyfriend who was in the Marines. The military dude was beautiful and would pick me up when he saw me on the street and bring me inside.

What is it that you're confused about? Jo asked.

I mean, what do you think being a muffin means?

It means she didn't know what to do with you, Jo said.

I watched her eyes, she was stoic even when she was pleased. Her jawline worked into a smile. She looked at me.

Don't worry about it, she just misread your masculinity for dominance. Common problem.

Really?

Yeah, you're just a bottom. That's not bad.

Okay, well, just the same, I'd be happy if you could talk me through using a strap-on better or something, I'd said, because I didn't want to be sweet and weak. I thought maybe I'd find strength in a sex act. I thought maybe Jo could help. I wanted to learn. I was getting man-ness projected onto me and I thought that my inability to fulfill whatever that was demonstrated a personal failing.

I've always appreciated what Paul Preciado says about masculinity: it's about giving death, the ability to give death.

In a video of Preciado delivering a talk (I've honestly watched this so many times) they ask the audience whether or not they'd like to, on behalf of the state, be givers of death or uterus production machines. Preciado says that they themselves don't want to bring death on behalf of the state, and they don't want to be a life factory for the state either, so they just shrug.

Recently, Hank and I watched *Married At First Sight* together from our respective homes. He often says, well, you're the man, to me, while he comments on how the contestants are behaving, you have to set the emotional tone.

We were talking on the phone about the most recent season while he was walking his dog—a Blue Lacy that he adopted because that's the state dog of Texas—and he ran into someone on the street.

DADDY BOY

Hi man, he was saying, yeah, nice to see you, yep, I'm talking to my oldest, he'd said. Thirties, he said, can you believe it? He was carefully not gendering me and it was nice. Yep, my oldest is getting old, he said, and I could hear Hank's friend agreeing in the background because he couldn't see me.

Not long ago, I spent time with one of my closest friends, Clay, in a green sulphur spring that was kept in a barn. We were nowhere. We stood in a field surrounded by short brush and farm equipment, the barn was a few frigid yards away. We stood in a stiff wind that raked at us over this massive, thin lake. We hadn't seen each other in too long, a year or more. We stood there for a few moments before stomping toward the barn.

I've always been impressed by the strength in Clay's body. Their hair lands on their shoulders now that they've let it go long. I envy how they hold themselves out like a point, bright green. I yelled into the wind to ask them if they feel like I do— like unclear about growing up into trans adulthood. They said, yes, absolutely, but they'd surrendered to the idea that they were constantly fighting how others saw them. Now, I guess, they said, I'm okay with letting everyone see me as they do. I don't care anymore and I still do. There's nowhere to go, they said, it seems. We swam around in the green water that was intensified by the reflection of gray walls. There were chicken wire windows, and a blue carving of a wave that was painted with a request: respect these healing waters. The words lilted up. The temperature of the pool was 98.9 degrees. It wasn't warm, there was no door that shut completely. The hunk of barn slammed around in the wind, the metal roof thudding. A group of people ran through the door in heavy snow boots and emerged from the stalls holding tropical towels, shivering. Clay had kept their shirt on. I was topless. There was something missing. The water was too lukewarm, too much like being in our own bodies.

Clay backed up to the hot water spigot and stood under it, the warmest place in the pool. Becoming part of the two-spirit community made them feel much more sane, they'd said, they'd rather focus on that. They said they'd spent most of their life worried about gender on individual terms, but not enough about community. Now, there's community and culture for me. This is growing up, I guess, they said.

Clay was talking about our coming out. We'd been children together—were babies when we met, with haircuts that Clay would give us all and tattoos. We called each other buddy endlessly and wore little ties and idolized leather Daddies and we were very angry but also laughing a lot of the time and falling into piles of arms and legs and wrestling and sleeping and just having bodies for the first time.

Clay and I didn't stay long in the spring, just towel-dried over what looked like a cow cistern. We smiled at each other and shook.

DADDY BOY

I didn't want to leave them. I drove myself back alone, wondering what it would be like to actually feel grown. Everyone in my family talks about how I've always been an adult, you've always had to do things on your own is the refrain. How would I know what it is to be grown if I was never a child? My hair was still wet and freezing at the ends, my underwear was, too, I could still feel beads of sulphur on my thighs. The idea of adulthood has always left me breathless. I ran my hands along the thin, crusted upholstery. I put my finger in a hole in the fabric on the driver-side door, my habit. It's a crusted gouge about the width of my pinky. That car was still filled with pac-marks from the days when I smoked cigarettes and drank, I left reckless burns every time somebody ripped me out of the driver's seat, took my keys away. A yellow foam peeked out of all the holes. Home? Sometimes, when I think of all those things, I want to park the car in some shallow brush off the road, take my hands off the wheel, put my palms on my thighs, let my brain empty out like a barrel.

One of the things I was very clear on as a kid was not to look like a tourist. I'm talking about the place where my mom worked and lived, a tourist area, where wealthy people summer, and immigrants and working-class people maintained the lifestyles of those wealthy. In this place, there are three million visitors every summer. Not acting like a tourist meant walking in a certain deliberate way, and having a particular type of speaking where you use lots of first names with no last names. Like, oh yeah, I was talking to Earl.

Truth is, I was always just visiting. I'd get found out if anyone asked me what school I went to and I'd have to say my dad lives in Dallas, and that's where I went to school, which is and isn't true. Except, whenever I'd say my mom lives here, I'd get forgiven because apparently, wherever your mom is, that's where you're from.

When Derek had explained my presence on my first day, he'd done it by saying this is Emerson and he is a writer. And I felt immediately that sense of belonging and disbelonging I'm so used to, like how the tongue goes back to any injury in the mouth. This might actually be a book about that grief.

Every time the van door opened, Cool Ranch Dorito smell made its way out.

What did they think I was writing about? I loved the comfort of being separated by "writer," but it also always felt like an end. Maybe I should have introduced myself by saying that as a kid, I was fascinated by Warren Faidley, the photojournalist who took pictures of storms and sold them. They would have known who he was: his pictures are really famous, black vortex over a yellow sky. In the early '90s he made an art and a killing and everyone realized this was kind of gold. Freaks of nature, slow shots that slide into blue.

Somebody's always watching, I thought when I first saw the photos.

One book about storm chasing says, all hyped up, that tornadoes are nature's attempt to restore balance. An elusive predator, it says of severe weather, and tornadoes specifically. The hunting metaphors are impossible.

In middle school, I wrote to Warren all desperate from my bedroom floor. He wrote me back something really simple and signed, a postcard that I kept on the sill of my trailer-sized window in the duplex.

When I was living in LA, I used to wait for a cloudy day to walk to the Arroyo. It was a place near my house where water was carving a V into large concrete slabs the width of two semitrucks in places, hardly a yard across in others. This trickle loped under concrete bridges and was caged in, there was a chain-link fence that ran high along the concrete bed. A dirt trail ran on either side of the fence, along the brush and elderberry and low hills. I'd walk to this trickle and peer over the bridge at the dribble that snakes, furry with algae, past flaking palm trees and runners in neon, a stream of cars somewhere, everywhere the buzz of power, rats rustling, someone bumping a basketball against a garage.

This water was so dangerous they caged it, dangerous because it flooded the banks in the late nineteenth century, caused death and destruction, and after that, city officials decided to concretize the Arroyo in an attempt to rein it in, to eliminate the possibility of more flooding. In the process, they destroyed miles and miles of wetland habitat, created a polluted runoff situation at the beaches. They're now in the process of removing the concrete in some parts, revealing a kaleidoscope: in order to return the environment to its earlier state, people who live along its banks are being kicked out to make room for more bike lanes.

Sometimes there was a sunset that framed the mountains, bright like bodies. The feeling of all that sun was like someone drawing with a broom handle on the bottom of my foot, swelling like filling a tub.

What happened with the Arroyo was that the city of Los Angeles got scared and got controlling, attempted to close off the flow of mountain water to the sea. It has arguably kept a flood at bay, so I guess it's been working, like a clenched jaw— the concrete they poured decimated all that had depended on that runoff to grow, and then, a new environment had become dependent on the concrete habitat, a human dependence in some places. When does the idea of "nature" not apply? I'm back to thinking about power and powerlessness.

Jo got me that book called *Thunder & Lightning: Weather Past, Present, Future* by Lauren Redniss like six years ago now. Her illustrations are almost as exciting as this subreddit that I love, r/submechanophobia, all about that freaked-out feeling some people get from seeing human-made objects that are submerged or partially submerged in water, like with the *Titanic* CGI. There're arguments that it's a brain thing, but nobody seems to know where exactly this "phobia" comes from. On the reddit, there're thousands of images of machines and other human- made objects (ladders, amusement park pieces, enormous drains) submerged in water. This is what I look at when I'm not writing. It's absolutely the most amusing thing I've ever played with on the internet. I clicked on it to get examples to write you about and now I can't stop scrolling. I'm horrified by the images of people jumping off of enormous hulls of ships (because of their proximity to the enormity of the hull that's just a skyscraper in the water) and delighted too. I dream about it all the time: water touching human-made objects, water where it's not supposed to be.

Redniss's book has all these complex drawings of lightning mixed with sections in verse and squiggle drawings of people. At one point, just before her chapter on weather and profit, Redniss tells the story of a man named Ben Livingston, who'd returned from Vietnam with a Navy Commendation Medal for a "weapon system under development…" It turned out he had discovered a way to control rain. When he got home, he opened a commercial cloud seeding business called San Luis Valley Weather Engineering Inc. He'd work for Coors Brewery, for example, with the mission "to make it rain as much as possible during the growing season, and then, through the end of the growing season, to try and prevent it from raining so that the grain—the barley that they use for the Coors beer—could mature with a very bright amber sheen to it. Make it rain until the fourth of July, and then from the fifth day of July until the harvest, to kill all these clouds."

Redniss details how at least forty countries all over the world are operating "weather modification programs." Beijing Meteorological Bureau used "cloud seeding to ensure a rain-free opening ceremony for the Olympics," for example.

On one page, a yellowing man is holding a pink cloud. The quote coming out of the man's mouth is an excerpt from *Dr. Lively's Ultimatum*, a novel about weather control written and self-published by Livingston.

The protagonist in the novel (himself?) at one point says, "Our mission is to defang, tame, wear down, and finally destroy that deadly poisonous cloud as it heads westward."

I wonder what our tourists would think of this language. Is it possible to adventure toward these storms without the desire to tame?

In her last illustration of Livingston's story, Redniss quotes him talking about his childhood, his life on a farm growing up. He'd explained how he'd go watermelon stealing and once told his dad he thought everybody should be able to get watermelon if they wanted it and so he and his dad planted rows of watermelon next to the road so people could just have them.

"If it didn't rain exactly when you needed it, those water-melons were always smaller," he said. "But they were much sweeter. So it wasn't always bad that it didn't rain when you wanted it to. I mean, as far as watermelon was concerned."

I think I've loved intense weather so much because it seemed uncontrolled—something that violent would quiet everyone in my house, would force them in. Would soften even addiction for an hour or two.

I can't say this better than my editor who, reading this whole thing, proclaimed at this part: "Yes!"

"Childhood, like intense weather, puts one in a state of being out of control, of succumbing, of being subject to the power of an outside force (in childhood, we're in the power of our caretakers; in weather, it's 'mother' nature).

But here, for you, you were put in a position where you needed to take control, be all-knowing at an early age, weren't allowed the kind of surrendering that we associate with childhood. And so sought it in weather, sought it in your 20s."

And she's entirely right. What an incredible thing to be read and to be seen! I wanted to be a child for all of my twenties because I hadn't been before. I was just reading a piece by Gertrude Stein where she'd written that the difference between adults and adolescents is the ability to be surprised. I'd spent my entire childhood with an all-knowing attitude.

Like I'd loved the *Parent Trap* franchise, both the Hayley Mills one and the Lindsay Lohan one, and how in both, the fake twins know best and trick their parents into an understanding of what's right. I'm sure it was not that fun to live with me. I thought I knew everything and nothing surprised me.

Hank doesn't know this:

I put my palm down and got glass in it while this person was talking about how to hit a Wiffle ball. Hank was with the boys in Dallas and Mom was still somewhere with Jeb and I was in the parking lot at the school where my grandma would drop me off every day. The glass was green and felt okay because it was near my palm. My fingers were warm and no blood came out because the glass held it in. I'd been picturing Hank's face as the ball. The other kids had their knees up and socks on. No one was smiling, but it smelled a little like sea. You could almost spot it: just a handful of blocks down, past the Amtrak and then the naval base.

Look, someone said because a seagull was now going for a teacher who was eating salad at one of those plastic-coated metal tables.

We didn't end up actually playing anything. It was just a demonstration.

Hank's face was the ball because I wanted to hit it. He'd let me down.

DADDY BOY

I was living with my grandparents in New London at the time, after Mom and I had to run away from Jeb.

Hank wasn't around anymore. He'd left with Tye and Gunner years ago, when I was six and Mom was off with Jeb somewhere on an extended trip. No one had sat me down and explained that this was going to happen. It seemed like I just woke up one day and nobody was there. I was alone in Sacramento and there weren't cell phones either and so I couldn't find out where anybody went. Hank was just gone and the boys were with him. It was over. I wasn't his. I was alone in that house in Sacramento and I came down the stairs to see those jelly jars on the counter with cartoons on them that we used to drink out of and sheets on the furniture and literally no one was there. I am only now getting memories back about how intense that was.

Besides hating the movie *Fievel Goes West* for its hypersexuality that sort of feels like a kid version of Chinatown, I think it bothered me so much growing up because Fievel falls out of a train in front of his parents and they move on really quickly and just keep on with their life, which reminds me so directly of this time in mine. Fievel spends the rest of the movie trying to get back to them but the family doesn't seem to care.

I was in a dangerous situation during that period, alone in the house with a babysitter and the slew of dudes she had over. I don't even really want to talk about it, but this is a crater in my childhood that has impacted my every day.

I felt the sensation of broken glass when I was in that parking lot thinking about Hank and blaming him. This is what he was talking about in his kitchen when he was saying kidnapping over and over.

Here's what I remember of fatherhood:

A sense of red: I could feel red-ness, whatever that is. Was it red mixed with black, was it paisley? The bed was so large and in a corner, with no space to walk around, blankets had to be tucked in with the whole body like a starfish. There were no pets except I sensed the feeling of a pet, maybe it was my brother. The TV was by itself on a table and had a gnome riding a goose on it. This image looped.

Hank was so big. My head leaned on his arm. I was three. I watched the gnome. My hair brushed his forearm. His blue T-shirt smelled soft and he was swinging me and singing. Light came down the stairs.

Go with the flow was his song. He sang it with four beats, go-with-the-flow, and then at random intervals, he'd let go of me so that I would explode onto the bed.

I loved him very much but I knew he loved Mom more. He was trained on her and she was trained on the boys and I'd put glue on my hands and peel it off.

I'd look at the wall while they went in and out, my body

weighted down. I'd stand and sense movement on either side of me. I wanted to control it. What was up the stairs? I have no memory.

The sweet smell of the boys hung on the couch. It was covered in a sheet. The TV was playing Nickelodeon's GUTS, our favorite show—that gauntlet for children built mostly of foam and plastic. There were foam mallets to hit each other with and enormous foam worlds that they had to race through.

This was me being left behind.

I'm only telling you this because this idea of disbelonging rises like bile. I look at myself in the mirror and catch my own eyes. Is it embarrassment? Is it humiliation? Hank had let me down. I felt as if it must have been because I had done something wrong.

Recently, there was a mouse in my kitchen. It was a deer mouse and didn't look so good. It was out in the day and if you went up to it, it wouldn't hop away, it would sort of come close. Its hair was wet-looking. My friend named him Oscar and without much effort, I eventually caught him in a bowl.

Oscar thumped against the walls of the bowl and I went to get my coat and I couldn't figure out which was more humane: do the driving thing where I take Oscar like three miles away or whatever, or actually kill him because the idea of separating him from his family ruined me. That's what the driving thing does, right? Like, was his family in my house also or my neighborhood at least and I was about to *Fievel* him?

When I came back with my coat, my friend who was visiting from Montreal was on their knees with the bowl and tears were rolling down their cheeks. Can't we just help him? they were saying, let him get bigger and then let him go?

I sighed like the caring was a burden, but I was also sort of relieved. My friend went outside to gather stuff for the plastic tub—we'd contacted an animal rescue lady on the island where I was living who I knew dealt with mice. She'd told me it was a juvenile deer mouse and yes, we could help raise it and then let it go when it was more ready, that it was a good idea. So we set it all up with twigs and bark and places to hide and a bottle cap full of water and a rock or two and all Oscar did was make his body into a curve and press against the most visible part of the clear plastic tub and die.

I want to be gentle. Am I learning or unlearning?

After I'd been alone in Sacramento for a month or two, Mom eventually came back. I moved in with her and Jeb and this whole other chapter started that I've already written about to you, which eventually led to me moving in with my grandparents and watching all the weather with them.

DADDY BOY

Here's something I never told you though.

One time, Jeb took us to an amusement park called Marine World/Africa USA. I'd found a feather on the ground and was playing with it. He put me on his shoulders in the parking lot on the way back to the car and I pushed the sharp end of the feather right into his eye. He tossed me off so that I flew.

Now, there is a man in a white Chevy Impala with Texas plates and a University of Texas hat looking at me. He's parked a foot or two from the curb to leave room for a just-dead mockingbird, one leg in the air. I made peace with Texas, a little, a little, Derek was saying. Back in the day, I peed on Texas—like I took a pee and then I spent four and a half years badmouthing it, and it always kicked my ass. But be not in fear, he was saying to Samuel, I am a motherfucking papa bear. Samuel laughed facing the gas station and didn't seem to care.

We'd stopped at a gas station with only four or five places to park.

All sorts of things fell from the van when we got out—Oreos, Big Gulps. We tossed them back in and then held our own shoulders against the breeze—hot or cold? Almost too fast to tell.

I'd badly had to pee, so was trudging in there and then felt a lump underfoot—this wing.

I knew it was a mockingbird before I looked, had to be, gray belly, dry under-feathers, black beak that opens into two hundred different songs.

The state bird: "A fighter for the protection of his home, falling if need be, in its defense like any true Texan."

I looked up at the man in the Impala. He'd been staring at me. The man was staring so intently.

I think of EZ Burger next to the El Fenix and the nest that was outside it. The birds were so loud when we'd be in there drinking from styrofoam cups and playing Cruis'n World. This was across the highway from our house.

This bird was warm under me and perfect—had just died I think, but no hole was anywhere and no bugs yet.

I took a Cheez-It box from the ground and ripped it into a gurney. I threw out the bag of crumbs and lifted the bird up. Its eyes closed just slightly.

The median there, or the strip under the gas station sign, was the nice kind with wildflowers like honey.

I set the bird in one of those clutches of wildflowers, pulled the box away.

Derek had just finished telling the manager of the Sonic that it was too fucking hot for the employees to be running to take orders and stuff. What are they running for? Let them walk. I'm a meteorologist and I'm telling you it's too fucking hot.

The manager nodded, shifted her hat (the one they were all wearing) and left.

Sonic is a special place, or it can be. Eating in the car is fun, said the Brits who had gone to order. They wanted to sit at one of the red tables by the little kiosk. I was about to get out and join them, I don't know why, maybe it felt too hot to sit in the car, when Derek was like, Emerson, can I talk to you for a minute alone?

Tony made noises like he was surprised and like he wanted alone time too, but he left.

I was eating my wet Walmart carrots out of their drippy bag.

I'd really like to talk to you about sex.

Oh, yeah?

Yeah, like do you have any dildos you'd recommend?

I absolutely do, I said.

Derek turned toward his computer.

Go for New York Toy Collective, I said pointing toward his screen and leaning forward. My friend Chelsea started that one and it's my favorite.

He found the page and I started pointing out the dicks that were probably best for anal, better for packing, all that kind of thing.

He was so excited.

I was happy when he started sorting through the colors.

These are my favorite for so many reasons, I said, describing the harnesses on their page that I liked.

Neither of us needed to know why the other used a harness and a dildo or wanted one.

This is so great, he kept saying, wow.

There's enormous energy stored in the atmosphere, said a sticker on his laptop.

Derek was still clicking around on the toy website when I sat back down in my seat behind him to look.

He was bookmarking all the tabs.

DADDY BOY

By the time Tony got back from the bathroom Derek and I had ordered fries to the van.

I watched my compatriots emerge from the central kiosk. June was dressed as Buzz Lightyear. The significance of her costume never became clear to me. I think she was trying to call the storms like the baseball thing with the inside-out hats. Moz and Jamal were shoving each other.

Everything around us slowed. The sky was an incredible blue. I watched all the other restaurant goers pause in their eating. My friends noticed, too, and started to play. They started doing pirouettes on the way to the van. Jamal and Moz linked hands.

I feel like a papa bear, Derek said again, closing his computer. He was watching people stare. That's my other job out here, I feel like.

You guys don't have to worry. He crossed his arms. The tourists were running like droplets.

Tony started up the van.

I have a lot of photos of myself with Jo still. She's at my college graduation. I'm in a binder and a collar at Joe's Pub, we're hugging. We did nine years of things together. I'd gotten to go with her to Lesbian Sex Mafia stuff and learn about breath orgasms and take a workshop with Barbara Carrellas, Kate Bornstein's partner. We did all this in New York.

I guess I keep saying the same thing: I was young.

S-M is amazing like this.

Kink was the first community that held me as trans, no questions.

This was in 2008 when everyone was getting raided because it was an election year.

I'd started going into session with Jo because I had no money and she'd pay me a little. This was before we'd actually gotten together. The first time, I thought I was just going to go over and watch her cat while she was gone again. But I'd got to her place and she was like, actually do you want to come?

I loved her apartment. She always had Lhasa de Sela playing. It was four hundred square feet and in Greenwich Village and she had a tiny fire escape with a basil plant on it and her black cat would sit there next to it and be proud. She had an enormous leather piece that she'd pull over the bedsheets as a way to make the bed kind of a couch. There was a wooden chest that neither of us were allowed to open because this belonged to her landlord and the deal was that he'd come back and use the apartment to have sex sometimes and Jo and I would have to leave for a few hours. Who knows what was in that chest.

I loved this purple chair she had by the fire escape, next to the radiator, which in the summer she'd fit with a wooden topper to make a small table. I'd sit there with Bustelo coffee at 11 p.m. smoking so happily. We needed each other, I'd realized at some point. She'd wanted to make me family. She was resistant the whole time about the age stuff, but my favorite feeling is winning someone over, so I'd kept on.

That first time, Jo packed clothes for me, dressed me up, put black makeup around my eyes, gold glitter on my cheeks. We were going to be courtesans, she joked, wrapping a cream-colored, feather boa around my neck. We were on Amtrak. We sat in the plush, blue vinyl Amtrak seats giggling, New York was slinking past us, expensive and furtive, wrapped in a strung-out popcorn smell. She looked like a Maya Deren film, a Vali Myers painting, like Vali Myers herself, with a font of red hair, red nipples, red pubis, black mustache tattooed onto her face, except not red.

Our hands kept brushing, my stomach was in my throat. I moved the bag she'd packed for me further under my seat with my foot. I tried to soften myself, make myself desirable, indispensable.

She told me, be cool. He won't touch you if you don't want him to. But would you want him to? Would you want to fuck him? Fuck him in the butt? Don't think about it too much. You're thinking about it too much! She pushed my knee.

My sexuality slipped between my legs, slipped out of my eyes, fell at her feet on the train.

She told me about the client, told me that he was sweet, has a wife and a few kids, a house in Montauk, one testicle. He couldn't have orgasms that involved erection anymore. She was teaching him about inner-orgasms, ones without cum, ones that shuttered through his stomach and hit behind his eyes.

It's like being a nurse, she said, a witchy nurse.

The dungeon was a rental above a video store on some otherwise empty corner. Amorphous pop music was pumping from somewhere, a vague tobacco scent hung onto leather curtains, red walls.

When we got there, the client was standing under a lamp in the hallway. He shook my hand, had a gray helmet of hair and a loosened necktie, looked like a newscaster, maybe was. I was holding her small leather handbag and imagining the three of us from above, the ugly hallway carpet, the nice man. He wiped his hands on his pants.

I got inside this cage, a warm cage on wheels that had a plush sort of bottom and was pushed against the wall. I was wearing a leather collar and black boxer briefs, had a synthetic, uncircumcised cock tucked inside an ankle sock that bent against my crotch. I was wearing a rubber top that Jo helped me into, squeaked as I shifted. My nose itched. I curled my limbs under myself and settled into the padding, pressed my face between the bars just to feel it, feel what it is to be a person in a cage.

When Jo patted my butt and said good boy, I'd crawled in, crinkled against the cage's vinyl inset, laid on my stomach, on my closed fist, a kind of grind.

Jo tented her legs in front of the man, she was holding needles, little tubes with medical-supply medium-gauge needles. I watched how she held herself, her movements weren't that different from anytime, from the Jo that made salads, she was just sharper, surgical, sweet.

She stuck one end of the needle into the white of the man's chest and sewed it out, she slapped the place where his fresh piercings were, blood spat onto her gloved hands. He made a hiss sound with his top teeth over his lip.

She held his cheeks between her forefingers and thumbs, cooed at him. His face gushed. He looked plumped by endorphins, his eyes lolled toward the curve of her, pouting, blood dribbling down his chest. She pushed him slightly and then pulled a flogger out of a black bag on the floor, drew it across his body before backing away. She wound up, pointed the flogger at his chest once, then fired. It came down on his piercings. His eyes shot open. He looked around for me.

There was a pause. I was supposed to be watching. He wanted to be watched.

I put my tongue behind my teeth like I was told once that models do.

Jo tossed her head back, smiled, twisted his nipple.

Look at our good boy in the cage, she said to the guy. We've got such a good boy in the cage. Her arm was over his shoulder and friendly.

Jo started bringing me in whenever she had a client who wanted this kind of thing. I'd put my little silicone bulge in their faces and they'd pretend to be squeamish. Each time, I'd get a little wad of hundred dollar bills, stockpiling them because the newspaper where I'd been working for the last year was basically over. The *Transom* editor would pay me for extra events coverage in little bags of loose tobacco.

This can't last long, I said to Jo. Sitting on the back of a bench in Washington Square Park after some Liz Smith event that she'd accompanied me to, I was breathing the smoke in front of my face up into my nose. I wanted to look sexy, I had my head turned to the side.

I've written this scene out a number of times, the one of us sitting together and reflecting as everything changed around us in 2008. I'd started falling in love with her, which felt similar to S-M because I was called to presence by it. I felt her falling for me, too, on this bench.

Shortly after this, I made a kinky illustrated book called *Daddy and Boy Wonder*—I don't know where it is. Does she have it still? She might. I used the same techniques I remember my mom using when I asked to make a book with her as a kid: we ripped paper into shapes. I did that.

I made these little characters that get flogged in the book and I think gave it to her for Valentine's Day early on.

I also wrote essays about age gap relationships and wrote a book about being concerned that I was doing what I was because of causality—hot mom syndrome.

My friends and I would joke that if this was *Rugrats*, she was Angelica, laughing at us like we were babies, and sometimes she was.

Can I tell you about this?

A few months before we broke up, it was Jo's birthday and I'd wanted to be alone together, but we'd needed the money or maybe she preferred going to see a client who had a pool versus being alone with me, I don't know. It had been years since I'd gone into session with her.

We went to this race car driver's house. He was thin and white, and had a helmet of hair. He was insatiably naked, was naked when we got there, wanted to be naked the whole time. He'd purchased his own collar, had it on.

The guy's house was weird and '80s, it was that same terrible kind of California ranch house that I remembered from a cocaine-fueled few years with Jeb. All the walls were white, white carpeting, glass and mirrors, sculptures, vases, and large metal cats with fake plants on them were lit up in the corners of the room.

I went to put our suitcase down in the guest room or somewhere, and when I walked back in, the client was hungry and on her, which makes sense, it was consensual. He was drinking a beer, holding it by the neck. I felt flooded. When they heard me at the threshold, they looked at me like parents do. I blinked and flushed. I was a blur. I stood very still and near the doorway. I dug the nail from my forefinger into the top of my thumb.

They both looked at me for a minute. I smiled as genuinely as I could.

Everything was fine. We were all adults, all consensual. I was twenty-nine. They were going to drink from the two thirty-racks of Corona that he'd lined up in three distinct rows in his fridge, nothing else fit in his fridge, it seemed. We'd set up a small ladder at the tallest point of his house so that I could stand on it and throw tennis balls at his dick. We were going to eat sushi for dinner, everything was fine.

I'd grown some muscles since that first session a decade ago, my muscles moved under my shirt. I'd gotten some more facial hair too—not HRT-related, just because. I imagined myself their equal but couldn't feel it. My wife—Daddy— was extremely powerful and wielded an amount of sensual attention that seemed unbounded. I'd never before been envious of this. Was it her command?

The house was so stuffy. The light in the room was so bright, plastic slats on the windows shook from the air-conditioning. This felt like such a weird thing to do totally sober. I was grateful to be sober, just unnerved.

When it was time to fuck him, he dripped back from the bathroom and flopped onto his back on the living room's cream-colored couch. Jo was set up next to us wearing a harness. He spread his legs and I grabbed him by the ankles.

Be nice, Jo said, which surprised me.

It must have been the way my face was. I was imagining shoving it in his butt in such an unfriendly way and quick.

Interstate 5 loomed since I moved to LA, I-5 North,

Sacramento. The haunted feeling I had about being left in Sacramento showed up in the angle of the light and the way the heat worked. I was reminded all the time. One day, after we'd gotten divorced and I moved into a place by myself for the first time, boxes all over and furniture covered in sheets, I was suddenly struck by body memories and I couldn't move. This had never happened to me before. I couldn't look around, I couldn't get up from the couch below the one window in the apartment. Had I been using Jo to block myself from having to experience this? She'd been a shield. Now I was all alone, and I couldn't access my body because I didn't know how.

I called a friend of mine who was a Vietnam vet. He shared often about his experience with PTSD, particularly about fireworks, which we had lots of in east LA, and what happens to his body and how the feeling passes. He stayed on the phone with me for hours, until it got dark, and then I guess the triggers went to bed—I've always known I had a certain terror for afternoon light, made worse by being back in California. My friend was like this is PTSD, it will pass, it will pass. He almost sang to me, this older man with a ponytail. We hung up when it got dark and I was feeling better.

I called Hank to ask him if something happened to me around that time of year in Sacramento and he said do you remember that babysitter who had trash up to the roof of her car? My sense memory was about the babysitter but I hadn't told him. And he explained how long I'd been alone and his guesses about what happened.

DADDY BOY

I was just explaining to a friend the other day that California was a minefield of this for me, thoughts/memories shook through the light like shards.

Still, I lived in LA for almost ten years like a toy with little pieces of broken shit on its insides.

This guy, his house, the whole thing was so direct.

He was curled up, dripping with want. I hated his dripping.

Woah, Jo hollered because I'd stopped before he came and just said you're done and walked away. He wanted to be topped, but I guess Jo didn't think I was going to do it like that, like top him by taking pleasure away. They both laughed. I heard her slap her leg, couldn't tell if she was impressed or angry. I kept my back to them. The white carpet crushed as I walked toward the guest bathroom. I pushed open the door and started pulling my harness off, white carpet, waterfall sink. I picked at my skin, turned on the water, and sighed. There was a small crack in the corner of the mirror, I put my finger in it, made a face.

Right now, I'm reading bell hooks's *The Will to Change: Men, Masculinity, and Love*. In it, she writes regularly about dominator culture and the need to be in control.

"Fatherly love is also about licking the child into shape," hooks quotes James Saslow as saying.

Her take isn't that this is positive—why is that the framework for fatherhood, she asks over and over.

I'd loved that Jo helped shape me, but I didn't want that kind of rapture anymore or that experience of being shaped by pain.

I just saw that somebody asked Lil Nas X on IG if he was a top or a bottom and he said that whole thing was toxic masculinity and he doesn't buy into it.

Power: to be able.

Surrender: to give up.

I made you, Jo said in one of our last fights and she wasn't wrong in lots of ways.

I'm talking about submission and vulnerability, and how some people don't have this in their day, they don't get to be small. They have access to so much power and privilege that they never encounter this feeling, which was the story for most of Jo's paying clients. And then, on the other side, some people are required to hold so much, to grow up so fast and always be right, that they never get the chance to let go, be taken over, taken care of, which was more the story for me.

DADDY BOY

Surrender is a spectacular feeling and worth paying for.

When Jo and I were first playing, I was shocked by how powerful it was, how enormous.

Toward the end though, I didn't want Jo to draw that power out. I wanted to do it myself, whatever that meant.

hooks continues in the book saying that people without dads often aim even harder for the hypermasc ideal. The longing itself "may give them a sense of quest or purpose," she says.

I certainly had that—I wanted to be the toughest, the biggest masochist, and would get angry when someone could take more pain than me. I was competitive. She'd string me up at parties and everyone would look and I wanted to win it all.

hooks laughs at this and says it fails. Grieving, she suggests instead, might move one's response out of the toxic realm. This quest to recover some kind of masculinity in one's life creates the illusion of control; grief, on the other hand, is a surrender.

"The patriarchal model that tells men that they must be in control at all times is at odds with cultivating the capacity to be responsible, which requires knowing when to control and when to surrender and let go," hooks writes.

I can't help but think about tourism again and Mady Schutzman who taught me about carnival culture—these large celebrations that are culturally and state sanctioned as places where merriment and bacchanalian frivolity are allowed to be unleashed for a brief period of time as a means, ultimately, of control. I learned from Mady that carnival culture is about giving the population a bookended period to get their jolly out (as my mom would say)— to be uncontrolled and wild, but in this very contained way. But bottoming was one place I wasn't touring, I'd committed.

One of the things I'd love most was that Jo would speak for me in social situations. One Halloween we'd gone to see the Procession of the Ghouls at the Cathedral of Saint John the Divine uptown. I was wearing this pink plush thing and a collar and we'd met her friends beforehand and no one spoke to me and she'd pet my head and talk for me if anyone asked anything. We got to watch the ghouls, a parade of costumed humans turned into creatures by the Mettawee River Theatre Company, and their "infernal puppets" as an organist played. They also showed a black-and-white horror film. That year was Dracula, I think. I had the fucking best time. I could just relax, take everything in. No small talk, no decisions to make. I felt like what it looks like to be a celebrity.

But here's the thing: Derek is supposed to get the people to a very similar place, a little scared, but also relaxed. What happens when he fails?

I'd outsourced this control for so long that when my feelings changed, I didn't know what to do—Jo sure didn't.

I'd fucked with our power dynamic and I couldn't go back no matter how much I tried.

"Love cannot coexist with domination," hooks writes.

One of our last moments of togetherness was at the Airliner in Lincoln Heights where there was a pride dance party for Dyke Day. I looked good, I was wearing this eccentric necklace a friend had given me along with the necklace that Jo and I had decided on instead of rings—we had gotten married the week before. We'd just had our photo taken and I was flirting with someone and so was she in another room—we'd never been monogamous. I glanced over and saw her smoking, she said she wasn't going to smoke anymore, but whatever, I'd figured, and went over to see if she wanted a drink. Just that second I saw her eyes roll up like shades. I was next to her. She started falling with the cigarette. I caught her almost but not good enough. She hit her head on the metal bench we were next to. The sound is still in my body. She was then in my arms and we were in a ball on the floor. She was epileptic. I knew this, but she'd only had a seizure one other time. We were in a small circle of gyrating people. She peed as part of it and that was her biggest concern when she woke up. I cradled her there on the floor for as long as she wanted. The cigarette had made a hole in her suit coat. She let me be the muscle to get us out of there, she put both of her hands on my wrist as I led us out.

In the van, I watched Derek force a smile. He watched the faces of the tourists and studied them and I watched them, too, their smiling—

Who is the dollar and who is the dime, Hank always said, meaning, if you think you're in charge, remember who is paying, that is the one who is in charge.

Derek was pulling the van into a field. He kept saying, watch your heads. I didn't know what he was talking about until I realized that we'd pulled under a singular cloud surrounded by blue sky with hail balls pitching out of it. They looked like skee balls, sort of rolling off the slope of the cloud to the ground and disappearing in a hot field. Honestly, it was a big catch. I don't know how Derek had spotted it from so far away. He also may have found the cloud and its hail by accident.

His eyes were red by this point and I'd gotten used to the hair by his ears looking wet always with sweat. I'm sure that I smelled. I am a strong smelling kind of person who forgets deodorant but shouldn't, I guess. I'd been sharing my smell with them for days now probably. Tony and the Brits, as Derek called them, always smelled so showered. Their freshness mixed with the dirt smells when they pulled open the van door that looked onto the rolling hills and this hail.

What's that 1994 movie about football misfits? Why were there so many motley crew sports movies in the '90s? This was the football one but it could have been the hockey one or the baseball one, but I watched this ritual unfold where Derek was like, go, go, go to everyone and all the people who had been on the tours with Derek before, which meant everyone except Jamal and me, ran out and lifted open the back door of the van and got into a cooler I hadn't noticed. They emerged with three sets of football helmets and pads. June was so excited. Jamal followed them out and was skipping, lifting both feet off the ground toward the pile of helmets. I wondered if all of them were older than I was. I would have to fight this enormous resistance in order to go out there and play like that. I couldn't find the willingness in my body. I watched them run around under the sheets of hail that had started to fall harder with their arms up. They were laughing so much and Derek was cheering them on and Tony even looked a little glad.

They're paying for this, Tony said. Their arms and legs were red with welts from getting hit around the pads.

They were having a delirious kind of fun.

I've never really known a relaxed state like this.

My friends from the van were open mouthed when the hail became tiny little bite-sized ice pieces. It was turning to slush. They were drinking it, or trying to and running like pinwheels around each other, shoving and laughing.

After this, we went to Walmart for ice for our coolers, which was sort of funny, and everyone was bumping into each other because they were laughing so much. Derek had started playing I'm thinking of a number between four and two thousand. This was only just the beginning of the day. We would get back in the van after Walmart and head south. I was excited by this route because we were moving toward Hank.

Derek was also playing a game where he'd swerve into the rumble strip. His other joke was pointing to one kind of animal and calling it another kind, he'd just pointed to a knot of birds and called them lions, cows had been bears for a few days.

There was a haze and it was already hot. I'd been sitting next to June all day, she'd had her military backpack on the floor between us, a pink neck pillow. Sometimes, one tree would stand out. The floor of the van was completely obscured by stuff, layers of trash and clothes by this point.

There was murmured talking, the talking seemed hopeful because we'd had such a good morning. June had her headphones in. Derek was fist pumping for no reason.

We have to ramp up the adventure, he was saying, joking and swerving. He was driving now. Sometimes he and Tony switched off.

DADDY BOY

He'd asked me by the bathroom how long I've been on HRT.
No time, I'd said, and he asked if he was offending me, I said
no.

This moment will be a good part of the book, Derek was
saying to me all of a sudden because he was happy about
the hail.

Want to see something interesting? Derek said and he opened
the window. Why did you do that? Jamal asked from behind
June. To prove a fucking point, Derek said. It seemed that he
wanted us to feel the fact that the wind was wrong. With his
open window, he pointed at something we couldn't see. We
don't have an eastern component to the wind, Derek said.
No tornadoes. Nothing. Still, he was positive that we'd see
something. There were three contrails. We'd turned Oasis
on. People were napping. The grass made sand gullies around
leafless trees.

That's a good-looking hill, someone said, I think it was Moz.
Derek said, want to go back for it? We can turn around.

They talked about how it was too sunny for a good shot of the
hill anyway and it was a joke about how oppressive the fair
weather is.

Trains! Everyone looked at a train poking through a field a few
hundred yards away, a joke too.

We were headed past Gem to Colby with trucks blowing us around. Everyone's arms had started to cross. Derek kept putting his hand under Tony's arm, near the pit, again, again.

June and Moz were eating ice cream out of old fast-food cups, I guess they'd gotten a pint at Walmart. There was something totally comforting about being in the van all day, I realized, looking at them. The grass was growing thicker. There was a fancy, realistic wheat rendering on the side of a silo, and only five colors to see total: white plus brown, green, light blue, black.

Yesterday, we'd spent two hours playing with a football in a gas station field. This was the end of week one. I got a tea. It was exactly like high school for me there—7-Eleven, football in the yard.

We'd sat under a shade structure with our water bottles blowing over and tossing a football and getting it to spin. A chase had been called by Derek and we knew it would be nothing, but we rushed back to the van anyway.

Apparently, he'd seen an indicator on the radar that maybe some cloud had precipitation in it. He'd said hang on a minute and suddenly we were spinning toward a CU field—shorthand for a sky full of cumulus clouds. That cloud is going up, Derek had said, but it just looked like a perfect Simpsons sky.

We waited like we had been waiting. We parked the van for a while near a cemetery to wait. Nothing was happening. None of the clouds grew. It got hotter and dust devils started showing up in the field near us—these little rotating columns of air that look like tornadoes but aren't. You see them while driving between LA and the Bay on the five, you see them elsewhere, too, because it happens when a pocket of hot air rises quickly through cooler air above it, making an updraft. Updraft is the same thing that makes a tornado, so they're cousins, but there's no mesocyclone with a dust devil. Dust devils are empty because they don't have this powerful vortex. It's like the difference between water whirling down the drain versus a whirlpool happening in the ocean. It looks the same, and is in some ways, the same physical processes, but one is only the hint of the other. Dust devils are thin, you can see right through them, but they are spinning and that's cool.

I had my hot tea and wet sandals and Tony started up the van to drive where Derek wanted. We turned onto a dirt road to holler at antelope who were staring at us from the waving grasses.

Cyclonic movement, Derek was saying. The plastic bags in the van disbelonged and were shaking. I was grateful suddenly that they were letting me come on this tour. I was happy and it made my arms relax. I felt my shoulders come down. I sighed.

I'm going to intercept this shadow, Derek said, he was joking. We turned back toward that graveyard. It looked like a mini golf course. Flat grass, green placards that felt weirdly corporate, mowed a few inches shorter than the corn around it.

We've got ground circulation, get your cameras out, Derek was saying. Everyone knew he was playing.

We started racing our own shadow in the van. We were also going to intercept our own dust. A tractor turned onto the road with us and we revved our engine as if to race. Tony's eyes were closed. He was wearing a shirt that said DOESN'T GET ANY BETTER THAN THIS.

Everyone was turned toward a field, watching a swirled wind lift up a handful of leaves. A beautiful joke. It was catching, lofting little pieces of grass. We chased the dust devils.

Derek was pretending it was something, and in a newscaster voice, was saying you can really feel the motion with this telephoto lens.

One of the guys got out to take a picture of a tree.

One morning I came down and nobody was in the lobby.

I stood around for a minute by the desk at the Days Inn and said a weird distracted hello to the people behind it. I caught sight of Jamal leaping into the air to catch something just outside. It was Moz and everyone. It was odd. No Derek, no Tony.

I walked into the heat, out of the electric sliding doors, past the van, which was parked under the concrete awning, and toward them all. June was in her full Buzz Lightyear costume again. She had the white plastic wings and the whole thing, green and purple accents. No one mentioned it. I didn't ask. Jamal was lying in the grass shooting a Nerf gun at Samuel, who was hiding behind Moz, armed with a football. He hit the small of Jamal's back, who put his hand back there and feigned injury. Jamal rolled over and charged Samuel. They chased and laughed.

Jesus it's fucking early, Derek said, coming outside. It wasn't any earlier than usual.

This storm has forty-thousand-foot tops, he was saying, swinging open the passenger side door. Let's wait for it to get organized.

Everyone went toward him, shifting slightly. Moz hummed and bumped camera equipment around in a bag. As soon as we got into the van, almost everyone closed their eyes. We'd tired ourselves out. It was dark like dawn.

You know, I'd done something not too dissimilar to this with Jo. I'd gotten us a trip on an Amtrak across the country. I was excited about it, was going to take us five or so days to get from LA to Boston. But we got off in Chicago and flew the rest of the way because Jo was very frustrated. We'd only traveled together like twice because we didn't have money for it. She got flown around the world by clients and I couldn't compete. I could pay for the Amtrak though, just not the nice cabin, the cheaper one with bunks. She was frustrated that the windows wouldn't open and also here we were sitting across from each other with nothing to do but play cards. She ended up sitting mostly in the observation car and watching *True Blood* on her iPad while I felt sort of sick on the top bunk, trying to sleep.

There was one good storm though, a sexy one that happened near Kansas or somewhere right there, St. Louis maybe. The thunder couldn't keep up with the lightning because we were going so fast. The flashes gave the train the staccato movements of an old movie.

It was an uncomfortable ride that seemed endless.

Derek just then started clicking the little light on the van's roof. Clicking it on and off and on and off and saying things like, oh shit look at that CG (cloud-to-ground lightning) and pointing, and everyone laughed because he was making the lightning himself.

It started raining, the smell was perfect and thick. Derek was chewing a massive amount of gum. There's a tornado on the ground in Laramie that we didn't get, not enough roads, he was saying. Rows of grain. No real rotation here. We opened the van doors to look more at the rain. Rain shafts.

I took off my shoes and felt happier. It started raining so sweet. The feeling was not that of danger. Twitter said another tornado on that first cell and a cell to our south touched down. How many more days of this were there?

Derek was eating so much gum. This was starting to feel like we were lost. I could see Jamal breaking apart a wrapper from a straw very slowly, in small squares. Moz clicked around on his camera absently. Samuel's jaw was fixed. We stayed parked under the cell for a while, lightning lifting up and over. See the scud rising into it? Derek said. That was something, he said. No one looked up to see.

It looked like the sky was going to eat. Derek pointed at vans and cars on a hill. If this gets going, all of them are deceased, he said.

Nothing got going. But the sky did look like it was coming in. We kept getting close, then every single storm would dissipate. The streets were wet. Puddles were everywhere. We were watching for wall clouds. Wyoming had a system producing tornadoes, we have broad rotation at the back of this, Derek said, putting another candy cigarette in his mouth. I want to get going again down there, he said, which meant we were about to drive a long time.

Everyone was sighing in the van. The drive was ugly. Derek got out of the car to sponge around, throwing clods of grass into the air. The rain hit harder, he was trying to use the clods to understand the wind.

On one of these attempts, a gust came in and blew the clod right into his face. We didn't see him wince but his shoulders did and Tony said, *oooh*. Derek wasn't done, he threw one last clod and stuck his finger in his mouth and then into the air to check on something. It wasn't clear what. He had a little skinned place next to his eye that was slightly bloody when he turned back to the van, a stick from a clod had hit him or something. I handed Tony a napkin to wipe him with.

We have one more shot tonight, Derek was saying. The plan was now to drive an hour and a half from where we were to another storm with a tornado on the ground. We were hurrying and that meant no stop. I was missing the thrill of the chase because I was over it that day.

We're done guys, Derek said suddenly then, actually, you know what, we're done. He wiped the tiny amount of blood by his eye.

Let's just head to the hotel.

It was so early, so light out. There was silence in the van. Everyone was on their phones for the first time, the hotspot in the van hummed. There were tornadoes nearby and we weren't close to them at all.

Everyone's mouth sounds were excruciating to hear. It was 6 p.m. We went to Applebee's because what else do you do. Maybe Derek's eye hurt.

I wonder where this kind of adventure flips from being vacation, like just enjoying that bit of hail, to trying to control things, capture them? There was only one time this happened: I was alone near a sixteenth-century castle with rectangle cut-outs that overlooked the sea for scouting. There were pastel-colored buildings with chipping paint and overturned dingy boats and yellow buoys that bobbed like bodies. The light off the water was perfect, it turned the backs of my hands an incredible blue. I wanted to marry the sea or fuck it. I liked and didn't like how it felt. It was July. I was totally alone and had planned it that way. Just me and the sea. I was turning thirty. My mom called me to say that she'd cleaned fifteen rooms or something, was on her hands and knees the whole day. Her knees were bleeding, she said, and then, I hope you have fun.

I'd cut the skin between my big toe and the next one, a thin gash with a flap that opened and closed in the salt water. I'd been swimming and so swinging my toe in sea all day, skin flaking off like pink breakwater. The seawall was being pulled away by the waves, little chunks. I bobbed in there and watched the water pushing at a line of boats. I was breathless, moving my legs in the dark. There was nothing except water all around, salt, and salt where my little mustache is. I was being eaten by it, everything in contact with the sea was being taken and eaten and pushed back. I looked at the castle and its tower. The tower was supposed to protect everybody from the sea, from danger that was carried to shore by pirates, apparently—an attempt to control what seemed impossibly open. The sea is our most open door, it said.

In the town, water sloshed on all sides. I cupped the sea to say goodbye, I wanted to say goodbye right to it, put my lips against its salt. I could smell the age in it, the ancient mud in there. A kiss wasn't enough. Children were playing nearby, lovers were huddled around thin paper circles of gelato. I was alone in the dark. The small lights from dotted restaurants in town glowed through the top layer of water. The depth seemed jarring, always does.

My instinct was this: find a bottle to put some of the water in. I wanted to fish a gelato cup from the top of a trashcan nearby. I could take a cup home, I figured. I could take some and house it, love it all the way, it would move when I moved it. I wanted to screenshot it, smell at it, uncork it for a second before stopping it back up. I'd do that until it grew dull and sour on my desk.

"We kill what we love," writes Hélène Cixous in *Insurrection de la poussière* (The Insurrection of the Dust). The book is a collaboration with Adel Abdessemed, an Algerian conceptual artist famous for his work *Who's afraid of the big bad wolf*, a sculpture made up of taxidermied animals mashed together in a frame the size of Guernica. He's also famous for *Coup de Tête*, a giant sculpture depicting Zinédine Zidane's 2006 World Cup Final headbutt.

"Zidane, that day, offered us a rapture," said Abdessemed in a *New York Times* piece. His work, which he frames as a means to spotlight everyday cruelty, gets him death threats all the time.

"I search feverishly for a way to flee the theatre of natural cruelty," writes Cixous in her collaboration with him. "This point of horror is situated in my chest, somewhere between my lungs, it dozes hidden away like a volcano, like a store of terror that would explode upon contact with certain images."

Recently, I was scrolling around and clicked on an article about keychains that house live reptiles—miniature snakes, turtles. They're in these multicolored liquids and are tiny. Apparently, the liquid is semi-nutritious and the animals are sealed into it in plastic bags around the purchaser's neck or wrist and live for a few days before they die. When they are dead, the purchaser is able to throw the animal-in-baggie out and there's no smell.

"We are bitten and we bite," Cixous continues. "What is a bit surprising is our vital need to misrecognize our natural cruelty. To not see: what we do, what we swallow, what we kill... Art is for opposing the vigor of separation, for making visible what we don't want to see."

I realize that my own screenshot impulse is about control. In my story about the sea, I left the water alone, let the memory ebb.

Are you sad? Derek asked June. I'm just tired and bored, she said.

If the tropical storm is pulling the low down, could I be wrong about this? Derek was asking himself while looking at his computer on its little swivel tray. We were now heading from Kansas to Colorado.

We'd taken the day off the day before because there was just blue sky and went to a waterpark in Garden City.

I skipped out on spending time with the group and hung out in my room, graded papers, smiled to myself, showered for a long time. They got sushi and one of them was left behind at Walmart and walked the ten or fifteen minutes back while everyone else looked and looked for him.

I was so deeply impressed by the stamina of these people. How is it that they want to keep going across the US like this? Are they ready for more disappointment? They run to it. They are running to it.

It was getting greener as we went north.

DADDY BOY

The cloud out of my hotel window was flaking off, it was cirrostratus, flaying, corn field adjacent, so much fucking corn! Soy, too, I guess. It was so sunny.

I was unsure about the waterpark, but it seemed empty, which felt ideal. I went with June. It was mostly what I expected, indoors and totally quiet. A lazy river fed into a system of plastic flowers and fish sucking air and spewing water.

It was 7 p.m. and very light out.

We'd vaguely made a plan to hang out. She was there with her room towel and I was, too, and we put them on the backs of some plastic chairs—I'd brought lap swimming stuff just in case but that was clearly not a thing, so I put my goggles and swimcap there, too, and we grabbed some tubes.

It was a quick ride, like ten minutes. I eventually got out of my tube and tried to swim freestyle alongside her—I'd just learned how at the Pasadena Aquatic Center, I'd taken one private lesson as part of my breakup strategy of finding hobbies, this was me practicing while June looped around. The waterpark was all enclosed by glass, so we were in a terrarium.

At the most exciting part of the ride, we went under this net into a plastic cave. In there, I was like, are you bummed we're not getting anything?

Not at all, she was saying, she loved seeing everything we got to see, the hotels, the restaurants, the farms, the people. She was like, this is my favorite thing I do.

I stood up in the waist-deep water to let a few kids go by.

Compared to June, the monotony ate me up, so much so that I almost didn't notice the plane wing sticking out of a person's yard in Colorado when we made it there finally. Remember that scene in *Twister* where the aunt emerges with a trail of blood and the scary arm of her sculpture broken but singing, was it a mobile? This looked like the feeling of that scene.

This was the day after the waterpark, the one that Derek had been hopeful about. We watched the sky make noise across a dead town and onto the road, hail pitching out, cold coming on. I get poetic at this part of the book, I notice: the tourists were a silhouette against this cemetery behind a granary, yellow horizon, Warren Faidley's orange. The trees were moving so fast, black against the yellow, against the wheat. The storms had been pushed south, so we'd headed back to Garden City.

Hey Tony, Derek said, have you ever done a human bidet? Works best with Perrier Lemon.

We were headed south to chase a real weak line of storms, the stratus clouds (rain ones) were spread all the way out on the horizon. We were quiet like we'd become, people were tapping their own hands.

I had sort of fallen in love with everyone in the van. I had nothing to say, but enjoyed the rocking back and forth we were doing. I wanted to see photos of everyone as children. I felt like we were in a school bus.

The dashboard was still full of everything, eyeglasses shaking on their visor clips. Jamal suddenly stopped scrolling on his phone and looked up. We got a tornado watch, people, Jamal said, but he was sort of sad when he said it because we were winding down the tour.

There will be storms in thirty or forty minutes, Derek said, we're going to try and get ourselves in position.

Derek had gotten Jamal a hat from the gas station that said STORM TROOPER on it, it was obviously not about storm chasing and had a Star Wars logo, but it was funny because Jamal really had been hoping for a tornado.

You're being a trooper, Derek said.

I couldn't believe I'd just let myself be taken around like this—I was wanting all kinds of food that weren't there and different clothes and a whole different way of sitting and being.

Had I not been able to hear those messages before, like before this moment in my life? Like the message of hunger was so quiet in my body. Is yours like that? The message to pee too. Those signals were extremely depressible for me. I could just press them down into somewhere else. I'd done that kind of pressing so supremely and for so long that I couldn't hear them really even when I wanted to. For a good while, I'd looked around for Jo instead of checking in with my own body. She'd been the one to be like, you should eat and eat these things, actually.

One of the clearest things about this trip had become those signals, like the "I'd like to be alone" signal, for example. I hadn't been able to hear that one before, but the constraint of the van was making these kinds of wants difficult to ignore.

I was on this trip in the first place because I had this burning desire to be. I wanted to explore the plains and to feel what it felt like to be back home, but I had no idea that it was also a project to learn about the body, these wants, or needs, I guess, like hunger and thirst. My entire childhood had been about gutting my body of awareness, making sure I didn't listen, so I was available to do what anyone else wanted. Trauma does this, chronic pain does too. That's why it was so nice to have Jo. She'd look at me and say you look hungry or whatever or even more simply, it's time to eat.

We were aimed at this storm and that meant no stopping for food. I felt around under my seat with my foot for anything to snack on.

DADDY BOY

In *King Kong Theory*, Virginie Despentes writes about moving the sex worker from the inside of the city to the outskirts so as to limit the animus directed at them, to control the people.

What is the animus? Is it physical? Is it that thing that beats in a body and signals life?

I wonder if Jo and Derek were taking clients on the same kind of adventure actually, if I'd wanted them both to do the same thing for me.

Is that what I mean when I talk about the ability to hear these signals from my body and to act on them? Did I want them both to lead me here? I think so.

The brush was glowing a sage color against rain that was starting.

Smells like shit, like easterlies, Derek said and it was true because the cows were downwind.

There were horses for sale, people were on their porches and porch swings watching cars pull in and out of this gas station we'd stopped at.

Tony swung the van toward a pump and I saw Jamal wince. We all heard scraping because Tony hit the yellow concrete divider between the pumps. Fuck, he started saying from behind the wheel, fucking goddamn.

Derek put his hands on his face and looked like he might get out and yell. He made a joke instead, something like shit, concrete is attacking us now, and Tony didn't look like laughing at all. He looked so sorry. His T-shirt hung.

There was another tornado tour group near us and they were pointing at the sky saying it could go from photogenic to monstrous so fast.

June rolled her eyes at them.

I want to just do this myself, to chase the storms alone, I was thinking. I absolutely could.

This is a hail monster, the other tour people were saying now.

Derek was like, okay, Tony, you got this and rubbed his shoulder as he sat back in the van.

I'm sorry man, Tony said, slapping his hands on the wheel for emphasis.

It's totally okay, you just get us to this new storm, okay? We 're going to try and get these guys a good cloud photo at least.

We started off away from the others and onto a dirt road. There was a truck that seemed stuck in front of us. Don't try to get past him, Derek was saying, let's just reverse, but we couldn't seem to. The van just slipped and spun.

DADDY BOY

We're going to be trapped in the hail core? Samuel said from the furthest point in the back.

The devil you know, Derek said in a main-character voice, cover your eyes and make sure you're away from the windows.

Rain was pelting the van to the point that we couldn't see. This was the most absorbed we'd been. I knew this whole thing. There were little pellets of hail, but it was too bright to be dangerous and there was hardly lightning. It was more of a car wash and we were more just stuck. Derek was clicking on everything on his computer and running models again and again. No one was talking.

We'd missed what Derek thought was a major storm with decent photo opportunities. As the rain stopped, the tourists were showing each other Twitter photos from the other chasers and exclaiming about how good it looked.

We eventually got out of the dirt by just going forward around the truck.

When we were driving back out, Derek yelled at a lady who'd pulled up next to the van, we hadn't seen him do that before. With every other person we'd encountered, he'd been available to chat and he seemed to love chatting. Seriously, it made no sense to fall off of that cell, Moz was saying. He meant we should have followed the storms. I wanted the tourists' irritation to mount. I don't know why.

When we came out of the rain, it was as if emerging from an oven. There was a sizable dent in the van and propellers from some small planes from some old storm maybe were stuck in a whole bunch of trees, horses eating or not eating, I couldn't tell. We were headed for one more tornado-warned cell that Derek thought we wouldn't make it to, but the tourists wanted to try, me too. A rain shaft was coming down, brown cattle matched the shrubs, their rumps did. It's hard to be wrong again and again.

We stopped for dinner at a quiet sushi and steak place that had *Dancing with the Stars* or something like it on all the TVs. Derek and Tony didn't talk.

The plains looked like work out the window.

Derek scrolled through the models. He seemed insistent that we try but also it seemed hopeless.

We aimed the van toward mounds of trash covered in tires, train tracks, an afternoon spread out like hands. We had no idea where we were going, just waiting for one cloud to pop, to make a mesocyclone, to eat some other ones.

I was baffled by the hipster coffee shop in Guymon, Derek took us there after sushi so I could get coffee on the way to this cloud, which was very nice, because he'd wanted to show it to me. There were rainbow flags and a little trans one by the register and also a jar on the counter that had a handwritten sign that said every time you don't tip a child gets a mullet.

Guymon, like every town we'd been to for a few days by then, had a central stucco building with broken windows. My heels were burnt red, legs sliced up from walking through wheat over and over on the way to the van. The sky was the only conversation. There was the minty smell of midmorning, late morning, but still. One of the tourists told me he went online and bought my book.

This is the strangest game: get people in a van for two weeks or a month or two and drive toward a single growing cloud for eight to ten hours a day. The cloud might not even produce rain, while one back where you started produces a tornado.

Out there, heat makes its own wind, a wind that plumes all of our shirts.

We wanted the deep blue of a storm cloud to eclipse everything, lowering. I could see this forever, seeing it once is never enough, those storm clouds that are so impressive that we hadn't really seen.

I can't communicate the color and maybe that's why I love it.

Give up, it's the end of the season, the season's over, said Tony out of nowhere. We 're not going to see anything.

What a dick, I said out loud and didn't stop myself from being audible because everyone felt like family by this point.

He was right though, the storm in Texas fell apart. Lightning flanked the road but in an ambient way.

I told myself I had to gather up my feelings. I wanted to fight someone. This was just too fucking boring.

I am an animal and I'll die an animal's death, Samuel said out of nowhere.

Tony, friendly now, said, You know, guys, there's a bug that looks like food, but it secretes something that makes the lizards and toads who eat it spit it out. So its whole life is entering mouths and getting spat out. Can you believe that?

The last several days of the trip went quickly. This was the end of everyone's tour even if they'd been out there for a month or more, these were the last two weeks. We spent each one the exact same as all the last. We'd go toward a cloud, it would dissipate, we'd eat at Walmart and Wendy's. I'd drink my motel coffee and have an apple, we'd make videos of each other throwing the football and June would put her Buzz Lightyear costume on every once in a while. I began to catalogue the bugs I'd killed in my notebook as a way to pass the time: I'd crushed so many ants in every parking lot and on everything, I'd killed at least four spiders in various motel sinks, I'd found an upside-down lady bug in my paper coffee cup after I'd poured the coffee in it.

Now, as I'm writing this, I'm thinking of this bug I killed that was helpless on my desk last night, belly up with all its legs flailing, just under my lamp. It'd been hiking the lamp's base for hours, slipping down the faux brass. It was the kind of bug that could almost be a tick, big with a large snout, shaped sort of like a spade. There was a red mark on its back that I liked, it flashed in the corner of my eye all day yesterday as I moved papers around to give it space.

When it flipped over, I lifted an envelope to its legs and watched it right itself and climb aboard. I was feeling friendly, helpful, and so, opened the door and put it out there on the envelope. I'd been watching its struggle all day, and wanted to relieve it, didn't think it through. I should have set it closer to the house. I didn't. I figured it would fly or something. I don't know why I thought that. I hadn't seen any evidence of wings. I left it out there and turned off the light.

This morning, the bug was in the exact same place I'd set it, the body was covered in a purple-tinged frost, mute and static. I watched the lump of body, glancing at it off and on for a half hour, telling myself I'd seen it move, the sun was out, it might be pretending to sleep. When I got up to check, I found that the bug was on its back, legs frozen up, dead body directly over the E of my name.

I'd wanted to be gentle.

My favorite night on the whole trip had been near the end. We'd gone to Burger King and eaten inside together and then there was a storm when we got back to the hotel. It was late like 10 p.m. and I'd gone to my room like everybody else and then twenty minutes later, there was a knock on my door, it was Moz with Jamal and June and Samuel wondering if I'd wanted to come out to the parking lot and watch the lightning with them. Derek and Tony were in bed. I went out there with them and there were fireflies just everywhere, the whole little hill adjacent to the Pizza Hut and UNOs and our weird Country Inn on a business park hillside was covered in them.

Lightning bugs, Moz said, and put his hand on my shoulder and on Jamal's.

The next day, near the panhandle, we pulled up to this bullet hole–ridden road sign. We'd stopped to refresh the radar because actually, it was looking good—we were in that special place in Texas that could have been anywhere—Oklahoma, Colorado, New Mexico— because borders are not at all real. It was our last day.

I'm gonna do something risky, Derek had said before he started driving. Around us was a molded town, Alamo-style homes, broken businesses. We're going back to Colorado, Derek proclaimed.

DADDY BOY

I'm happy when they're happy, Tony said, looking back at us, he was in the passenger seat this time.

It was a short drive, only a couple of hours, and as we neared where Derek wanted us to go, chase cars were lining the road alongside the doppler van. It's a van with a giant plastic measuring instrument on it that rotates, it's always deployed to decent storms, the most choice storms. This was the first time we'd seen it on the trip. The wind through our van was loud, there was sighing, some sun, with light on all of us, but pitch black behind. Because this was the unofficial last week of chase season, everybody was here.

We were stopped near a field of dead trees behind a granary. We pulled up beside a baby blue pickup with people in it that looked like they were doing the same thing we were.

I was looking at them when, from the back of the van, Samuel yelled wait, and lurched toward the door. He yanked it open and ran into the street that had begun to thrum with people arriving from all over. He ran toward a lump in the road and held his arms out toward the SUVs rumbling at him.

We watched Samuel pick up the lump in the last of daylight even though it was only 2 p.m.

A funnel was gathering up somewhere, that's for sure, that was the quality of the light.

Samuel ran with the lump to the side of the street and as he got closer, we saw a turtle in his arms pissing an enormous stream everywhere, all over Samuel.

He set it down on the other side of this falling fence and wiped his hands on his pants.

Pissed on me, he said when he pulled the van door open.

The wind swirled around.

I seemed to be the only one who was smiling for that moment. Derek and Tony were fixed on the radar—when the green and the red get together it's called coupling and indicates rotation in the cloud, the mesocyclone. That's what we're always looking for.

Let's go, Derek said, and he meant to the ridge just in front of us. Samuel's turtle had begun walking softly away from the road.

Someone was like, I think it's a land spout and not a tornado that's in this storm. Derek and Tony ignored the person. Land spouts are like dust devils. They're okay to look at, they really do look like tornadoes, but are empty of the power.

There were many vans pulled over in front of us and we joined them. We parallel parked by this barbed wire fence on the side of the road. Everyone was standing outside of their vans in windbreakers looking off to the north. There was an orange sky because it was almost sunset. The orange framed this thin gray funnel, one sweet one that sort of looped out of the clouds. It didn't thunder. A couple of rain drops fell on us. It was mostly quiet except for some talking like we were on the sidelines of a sporting event. We watched this funnel dance around at the horizon. We were all pressed against this fence just off the curb. The funnel was a football field or two away. Moz was busy with his camera. We were quiet. There was still tension somehow. Another funnel or two dropped down around this one momentarily, they danced together in the orange before springing so quickly back up. Everything went too fast for me, I'd like to have sat in it, sat in the mud beneath the funnel with no clothes. I wanted to be much, much closer.

The funnels were all small, not really whipping anything up. It lasted for ten minutes before we started to hear people opening sodas in other chase vehicles because the storm had gotten so still.

After a few minutes, Derek just said, well guys and leaned way in to the front van tire to pee. It was clear to everyone that's because he was relieving himself of the burden.

When we got back into the van, Derek was saying, Your cells expand, meaning human cells expand during tornado events, to Jamal, who didn't seem as jubilant as I'd imagined. Turns out, nobody really felt that climax because these weren't actual tornadoes.

Almost immediately, there was debate online about whether or not that storm was actually just made up of gustnadoes.

"The term 'tornadoes' is probably a little generous for these," wrote a chaser in a blog post right after the storm. "As they were weak spin-ups without condensation funnels."

That was a tame post, apparently. Another chaser was saying he was pissed that he'd stuck around for the landspouts and missed a tornado elsewhere: "Landspout targeting was not in my plans... I finally got antsy enough to bail on it," he said, alternating between calling them "dustups" and "landspouts" — neither of those are tornadoes at all. It's a house cat to a lion, June said behind me.

Derek and Tony looked at each other when she said this. We hadn't seen a tornado technically, just seven vertical gusts of air.

But we'd already had the ceremony where we put the hand-sized tornado decals on the side of the van and no one was going to take that back.

When it was much quieter, Derek and Tony stood around the van to call the people they were dating. I hadn't heard them do this any other time except that night through the motel door. The coupling on the radar dissolved. The sand around us had turned pink in the dark.

Skeletons of farm equipment were framed by lightning, puddles everywhere. It had been raining for a few hours. Derek kept talking about how everything's better after you see a tornado.

I just spent forty-five minutes watching top ten lightning strike videos on silent, I love the squash of purple that comes from the bolt in the frame. The human, storm-lover or horrified, doesn't matter, always shakes in proximity to this bolt. Always. At least, the camera does, it seems involuntary and fixed. I'd assume more videos would have the moment when the person drops the camera and runs. None of that happens. The person shakes, the camera shakes, the world does. Everyone is fixed for seconds, everybody.

When this whole tour thing was over, Hank picked me up in Oklahoma City. All of a sudden, as we pulled toward Tye's place so I could pick up my dog, this storm hit. It was the best storm I'd seen the whole time. Rain was pouring off the parking garage and swamping the planters. Cars were taking shelter around us, driving into the garage to keep away from the lightning that was cracking and cracking like bombs. The lightning was flashing so much and then the hail came. It was golf ball-sized and then baseball. Two people ran into the parking garage with their purses over their heads, they laughed because this is Texas and everyone knows it'll pass. Still, the tornado sirens came on, which means someone spotted a tornado on the ground. It echoed through the car. Hank is never afraid of this. We sipped our coffee.

In that remake of *Parent Trap*, Lindsay Lohan had this whole big moment in the car where she'd felt around for the word *dad* in her mouth and then tried it on her bio dad, who'd missed the momentousness because he'd thought she was the other twin who said it all the time and so it wasn't interesting. I haven't talked to you about him much in this book, but I remember trying this on my dad too— like, wow, what a wonderful word, I'd said it to him in his Jeep. We'd been singing in the car. We both knew that song from Jewel and he had her on tape. While we sang, he cupped my ear so I could hear myself—you sound so good, he said. Listen, listen—that's you. His hand was so warm there on my cheek.

I felt a huge amount of responsibility for this relationship and how it went. I'd tried forever to get it back. This trying had framed my life till now. But I've surrendered.

You know I love you so much, I said to Hank in his truck in the parking garage.

I know, he'd said and laughed.

We watched the rain pitch off the second story of the parking garage onto shrubs outside, swamping them.

When I'd finally left Dallas to go east at seventeen, he'd been the one to put me on the plane. It was his way of saying sorry for everything, how I'd had to leave his house and the safer space he'd made for me, and how he regretted it all so much. He waited at security for me to go in, a crowd of people blocked most of him from view, so he kept moving to find me as I wound my way through the scanners and the X-ray thing. I kept looking back and he was moving around to see me. He kept finding my face. His was turning red. He'd put his hand up. I thought he'd leave after I got through the metal detector, but I kept turning back and he was still there. I saw a tear make its way into his mouth. He waved with the pad of his hand, tears streaming down his face.

I'm proud of you, he'd said suddenly in the truck.

I waited.

You were always trying to kick yourself out, he said. I think you're finally realizing that there's nowhere to go. The grass isn't always greener. He pinched my shoulder and shook my arm, proud of you, he said again, and I think he meant the divorce.

• • •

I felt guilty for much of my adult life because apparently as a little kid, I was a know-it-all and I would tell on Hank. I'd go to my mom and say he did this, he did that and he jokes about it now, that I was so annoying. I always thought I could do better than him, even as a six year old or whatever. I'd draw angry pictures about money being a monster and credit card debt and divorce, because that's what I was told our problems were, and now I have credit card debt and a divorce and I've done all sorts of other things that my childhood self would have told on me about.

Hank always said that he almost left Mom on the day they got married because they had an enormous fight, but he looked at me through the fighting, I was two and he decided I needed him, I looked at him like I needed him, he said, and so he stayed. What power I had!

I don't think siblings like when one has power. I didn't want it to begin with. I've been chasing and running.

Could a soft storm just come and take me up? Deliver me from all the work of my insides? Make me weak? I love when it envelops like a mom, it blackens the sky in the richest, most wonderful way, takes away worry, holds me by the neck, at the back of my head.

I let my limbs relax.

DADDY BOY

It's COVID and in the place where I'm living right now, there always seems to be a handful of ladybugs stuck to the window, I try to open it to let them out but all they do is shuffle their wings. When I take my jacket off the nail by the door to put it on, handfuls of them emerge from my jacket sort of sick, they've been flying in and out of my sleeves all day and crawling into the hole that was made for the cord of the lamp. They die in there, handfuls of them. I don't know where they come from, but they seemed to be born in there and are motivated to all the windows and doors by heat. They die in droves. It also smells like coffee at night which is an odd thing and the ladybug smell mixes with it—a grass smell—because they keep dying in the hot water I make for tea.

I can't really close anything off is what I'm saying. Mice come in all the time, they make their bodies dime-sized to join me in here. I wonder if I'd been swallowing ladybugs, they made their way into everything that I drink, it seems.

I've been thinking about all these mice and bugs and how as a kid, I'd be frustrated when anyone would get me any new toy that I hadn't planned to get—I didn't want any surprise toys because I felt obligated to care for them all. I had to sleep with every toy anyone had ever given me so that no one ever felt lonely, which meant I could always barely move.

Right now, I have another mouse in the kitchen and I know it because there are little foot tracks in the flour I'd spilled across my counter. I realized it just this second, just as the fireworks were starting up outside my window. I put some cheese in the little Havahart trap and put the trap, called Metal Cat, on the counter where I knew the mouse had probably gone.

I was induced for the fireworks. My parents at twenty years old were told by the doctor that it would be cool to hold me while the fireworks were going off on the fourth of July. I wasn't late or anything, but the doctor convinced my parents that it would be a cool moment and I guess it was, but still.

It's my thirty-fifth birthday today.

I caught the mouse in the trap just as the climax of the fireworks show was hitting. I heard that the mouse was in the trap before I saw it was in there and then watched it try to get its nose and limbs through the little slats. The mouse was upside down—it was everywhere, its arms were so small, its hands were distinctive and pink. I wondered if I should drive off with it, the two miles, that whole thing. But the sky was locked up everywhere with sound and with color. All sides were flashing, so I pulled the curtains closed and talked to the mouse. The scene seemed to go so slow, people were outside cheering through the smoke.

I held the mouse in the box and talked to it.

When the cheering quieted, I picked up the trap and slid open my screen door. A person was there, right on the porch. I hadn't noticed him—it was the mackerel man, he wore all camo and fished for mackerel off the dock near where I was living and he lived there in his van for the months when the mackerel were running, he'd collect cans, people would leave their empties by his van so he could return them and keep the money. I'd been doing it too. Can I tell you something? he'd said. I was still holding the trap. Sure, I said and the mouse thumped around. I was getting comfortable on your tailgate to watch the fireworks and I heard a thunk—I thought he was about to get angry at me for something, but he said, I think I broke it. He showed me to my truck, a frayed wire holding up the tailgate had broken under him. The last of the fireworks went off just then, the hissing kind. Oh man, that's okay, I said. It was about to go, no worries. Well, I'm sorry, he'd said, but thought I'd be a good guy and tell you, let me know if you want any money.

The crowd thinned. I walked with the trap to a scrubby place near the house. There was a low rock wall. I set it on the wall and opened the metal lid. The mouse had pooped so many times already. It looked at me all fluffy. It watched me for a while before climbing out of the box and into the bush just outside. This isn't what you're supposed to do, but I don't care. It slipped off like a slight smile.

You know, the only other time I saw locusts was with my dad. I was visiting him for the longest stint we'd ever had. We 'd only ever spent a handful of weeks together.

This was in Midland. I was seven. The whole visit, I had night-mares that he would leave me in his running Jeep like at a red light, and I wouldn't know how to drive, and he'd be gone, completely disappeared. I'd watch his hands on the wheel while he drove and try to learn. He'd leave me inside there without the key and go into a gas station at night and I was terrorized. What if I needed the key?

We'd go to the sand dunes that were just past town. You could get a pickle in a red-checkered hot dog carton and we'd stand around eating those before I played in the sand. I liked to watch the pickle juice run down his thumb. I remember being surprised by Dad's body. I always was when we hung out, it was a proximity thing. I was wearing those '90s sweat-pants that were feminized with a stirrup. The ones I had were a kind of red/orange neon and they went with this shirt that would become a new hue if you put your hand on it—a color change shirt. He'd helped me cut the stirrup off the pants and cuff them. Dad kept his cowboy hat on the dashboard. He'd walk me up to the top of one of the orange-tinted dunes. The enormity of desert. I think this was the Monahans Sandhills State Park. The little rivers made by the wind would shake. The sand had been blown in during an ice age to the Permian Basin and now it can't get back out, it doesn't spread to relief like at a beach. It stretches toward road instead. There's an informational video about Monahans that I watched, the kids don't care that there's no water here, says the ranger, but that's not true. I cared. Jackrabbits with ears all up ran around, making tracks that are soon wiped out by sleds—basically, you'd pretend it was snow and use a saucer. Some kids had kites. They sold the saucers at the same place as the pickles. I don't remember sliding down.

On one of our trips there, we rolled over hundreds of dead locusts in the parking lot. My dad had just finished telling me about the time a bird exploded on his passenger side mirror when we pulled in and crunched through them. They looked like little missiles, steely except for their front legs and this red behind their heads, was it blood? They were all dried. Dad said they feel exactly like wax paper. I wanted to protect him from having ever hurt anything. I wanted to cup my dad's cheeks, this guy I didn't see enough, and tell him it was okay the bird had died, it's okay he never sees me, it was okay these locusts ate each other, it's intense, but it's okay. I wanted to say all these things softy, but he didn't need me to. I needed him to say this to me, actually, but I was a child. I folded my hands and watched him drive.

ABOUT THE AUTHOR

Emerson Whitney is the author of the critically acclaimed *Heaven* (McSweeney's, 2020) and the poetry title, *Ghost Box* (Timeless Infinite Light, 2014). Emerson's work has appeared in the *Paris Review*, the *Los Angeles Times Book Review*, the *New Yorker*, and elsewhere. Emerson teaches in the BFA in Creative Writing at Goddard College and lives with a mess of dogs, his spouse, and his best friend, between the countryside and the sea.

To protect the identities of those in the text, names in *Daddy Boy* have been changed and identifying details have been altered. Certain scenes are intentional composites as a result. *Daddy Boy* was written via recollection, and all inaccuracies, including any meteorological or geographical errors, are purposefully left uncorrected.